that

Dwells in Me

Donna Hodges

The Spirit that Dwells in Me

Trilogy Christian Publishers A Wholly Owned Subsidiary of Trinity Broadcasting Network

2442 Michelle Drive Tustin, CA 92780

Rights Department, 2442 Michelle Drive, Tustin, CA 92780.

Trilogy Christian Publishing/TBN and colophon are trademarks of Trinity Broadcasting Network.

Cover design by: Karl Valcourt

For information about special discounts for bulk purchases, please contact Trilogy Christian Publishing.

Trilogy Disclaimer: The views and content expressed in this book are those of the author and may not necessarily reflect the views and doctrine of Trilogy Christian Publishing or the Trinity Broadcasting Network.

Manufactured in the United States of America

10 9 8 7 6 5 4 3 2 1

Library of Congress Cataloging-in-Publication Data is available.

ISBN: 978-1-63769-636-1

E-ISBN: 978-1-63769-637-8

This novel is dedicated to the Holy Spirit, who gave me guidance, woke me up in the wee hours of the morning, showed me visions and dreams that I never thought possible, and blessed me throughout this whole process. Without the Holy Spirit, this novel would not exist. All praises go to my Lord and Savior Jesus Christ and our Father God, the Creator of our world.

View and Opinions

The views, beliefs, and opinions expressed within the content of this novel are solely the author's and author's alone. They do not reflect the opinions, views, or beliefs of anyone else, including the publisher and distributor.

The Spirit that Dwells in Me

S - Spiritual

P - Power

I - Interacting

R - Righteously

I - In

T - Truth

D—Delivering

W—Witnesses

E—Essential

L—Lives

L—Loving

S—Salvation

Acknowledgments

First and foremost, I must give honor to my Lord and Savior Jesus Christ who has guided me through life's transgressions, healed me when I was sick, uplifted me when I was down, never left my side when I wanted to give up, and introduced the Holy Spirit to my soul. He gave me revelations and prophecies since the age of eight, but I never knew how His Spirit dwelled in me until January 2016. The Lord God placed me on assignments years ago, and I had no idea what He was preparing me for. God's grace and mercy have brought me through things I never thought possible and allowed me to see things others will never see.

I must acknowledge my parents, who are deceased and dearly missed—Annie Wright and James Wright—because, without them, there would be no me, and I would have never been able to have the fullness of God in my spirit.

My husband, Terry Hodges, who has been my rock and has encouraged me to follow my dreams even when I wanted to give up.

My sons, Stephen and Darius Brown, who have always encouraged me in my writings and stood by my side when things have gone wrong.

My pastor, Barbara Brown, of River of Life Worship Center who has been my spiritual guide and confidant in the Word of God.

My best friend, Prophetess Pamela Hunter since September 2018. Because of her and her faithfulness to God, I am now able to distinguish what an assignment is and what God's plan is for me. She has taught me about being a "seer" and how God shows His wonders to those that are faithful and true to His Word.

My spiritual friend, Prophetess Renay Goodman, who is a true disciple of Christ. Her wisdom shows in every aspect of the gifts God has given her. From day one, she has told me what my dreams, visions, and outcome in life would be.

My good friend, Alvia McDaniels who keeps me uplifted daily when things are going wrong and senses when I need a friend to talk to.

My stepdaughter, Britney Hodges, who took the time to edit my work to perfection. For letting me know that she had never edited this type of nonfiction work and loved the testimonies I poured into this novel.

Other family, to include my uncles David Wright

and Eugene Wright, who I can always turn to when I need a listening ear or support. Also, want to thank my friends and supporters of my work that give me courage.

Table of Contents

PROLOGUE

Mark 13:32: "But of that day and that hour knoweth no man, no, not the angels which are in Heaven, neither the Son, but the Father."

The revelations of Jesus Christ have been upon us for some time, but are we clearly seeing the signs? His teachings on healing the sick, raising the dead, and giving sight to the blind are no mysteries in the Bible. For as we live out the plagues of Exodus and Revelation, the world that we know will never be the same. As God performed His miracles over time, there was one in our generation that we did not see coming—Hurricane Irma. This drastic hurricane caused so much devastation that the entire ocean in Long Island, Bahamas, disappeared on September 10, 2017. It caused serious destruction and damage to the island. However, God, with His tremendous power, was not finished. God took away the ocean on Long Island for the world to see. He removed all that was in it. People walked upon the wet ocean front, and within hours, God brought it back like a fierce lion raging after his prey. This was God showing the world that He still performs miracles like the days of Moses when God departed the Red Sea so the Israelites could flee from the pharaoh and his army. Miraculously, when the Israelites had crossed over to the other side, God caused the walls of the Red Sea to fall upon the pharaoh's army, and they drowned. God's messages to the world are clear and concise: Obey my commandments, or I will destroy the world again!

In Deuteronomy 11:26-28, God clearly says to His people:

> Behold, I set before you this day a blessing and a curse; A blessing, if ye obey the commandments of the Lord your God, which I command you this day: And a curse, if ye will not obey the commandments of the Lord your God, but turn aside out of the way which I command you this day, to go after other gods, which ye have not known.

Many people fear God because of the unknown certainties in life. Yet, there are others who have doubted God's existence from the beginning of time. These are the people who believe in the ideology to put their trust in man instead of God. Scientists would rather have them say, "There is no God." These people question whether God exists because they have not had an encounter with Him. They also may see things happening in the world, such as a baby dying in his mother's arms, houses being destroyed from natural disasters, a man being killed in the streets, or people suffering from hunger in third world countries, but these are the things Jesus gave His life for. God already knew these things would happen before they happened. It says so in His Word.

These people tend to put their trust in man and worship mankind. However, God's message to His people and the world is, "His Son died on the cross, so that we may be saved. We are all on an earthly loan. God never intended for this to be our final resting place. The people that God has placed in our lives are not ours." God put us upon the earth to be vessels for those that are lost and to help them find salvation. Who knows, maybe He placed us in their lives to be their angels and help them make it back to heaven before their lives end. That is what I believe about my earthly family. Had God not placed me in my father's life, I honestly believe that he would not have found his way into the kingdom of heaven before he died.

Throughout the Bible, there are stories and teachings about Jesus Christ. Yet, some still do not believe. They say, "Why put your trust in an invisible God that man cannot see? Or why worship a God that man told you to?" Some nationalities believe that their ancestors bore scars from those proclaiming

Christ's existence. However, they pour out their wallets every Sunday morning, helping them get rich.

I recently sat next to a young man named Victor on a flight from Baltimore, MD, to Charlotte, NC, on December 12, 2020. He told me all these things in life he wanted to accomplish. He was only twenty-six years old but was very resourceful in technology. However, when it came to Christ, he told me that he did not really believe in religion. He believed in science because a lot of things did not make sense to him. After I explained the difference between religion and Christianity, God's love for him, and showed him pictures of what the Holy Spirit had revealed to me in the sky. He was mystified. I told him how he could gain salvation on the airplane even while talking to me if only he gave his life to Christ and accepted Him that day. I told him, "Taking into consideration the pandemic and the uncertainty of life, wouldn't you want to be certain that if the rapture came today, you would be saved?" He accepted Christ that day and stayed in touch with me. We must be messengers for Christ and help those that are lost in the world before it is too late.

For years, I had been ridiculed and laughed at by family members because of the gifts God gave me as a seer when I was a child. It was not something I asked God for nor could even comprehend. I could not explain it at times. But, when God opened my eyes to a world where the dreams and visions started to come true, I accepted it, bowing down and worshipping Him. You see, I chose to worship God. I would rather worship a God that I have not seen than die as a sinner in eternal damnation and find out that God really existed. I fear God with all my might because God has the power to fulfill my every wish.

When God gave up His only begotten Son to a world of sinners so that we might be saved and have the right to the tree of life, I could almost feel His presence from the teachings I have read. I began to believe, trust, and live according to His Word as a child. God gave me sense enough to believe what the Word of God was saying to me and to my heart.

God said so in His Scriptures: "And all nations will hate you because you are my followers. But everyone who endures to the end will be saved" (Matthew 10:22, NLT). Many will not adhere to the Word of God, and they will fall by their own transgressions. But, as for the keepers of God's Word, we must be disciples upon the earth to deliver the Word of God.

The deceitful man will say in his heart, "There is no

God." They do not know God and have never known Him. For that, they will be cast into the pit and die in their own sins.

After sharing my vision with several people of God, I have been told that I should tell my story to the world because no man has been able to peek into the sun with a naked eye without going blind or having severe eye damage. But my experience was not of man; it was of God and the Holy Spirit. God chose me to see these things so that I will be able to tell what I had seen and get the prophecy behind it.

It is not a mistake that God chose me for this assignment. It was His will and not what man has been trying to do for centuries. Man may go to the moon and see a lot of things with binoculars and telescopes, but God allowed me to see it for myself with my own eyes. And, yes, my eyes did hurt for a few minutes afterward, but it was not a great hurt, and I accepted that, if I had gone blind at that time, it was well worth it because of what the Holy Spirit and God revealed to me on March 22, 2020, in front of River of Life Worship Center in Odenton, Maryland with many witnesses around me.

MY ASSIGNMENT BY THE HOLY SPIRIT

Writing this assignment has not been an easy task. If truth be told, I did not know what an assignment was until my best friend explained it to me. Though I had accepted Christ as a child and always been in His presence, I was never taught about assignments until I came back to Maryland in January 2016. I asked God to put me in the presence of the Holy Spirit again because I did not feel like I was receiving it from the church I attended in Augusta, GA. Though it may hurt the feelings of the parishioners, it is the honest truth. I needed the Pentecostal feeling of the Holy Spirit. When God heard my cries, He sent me back to a church where the Spirit was duly known, and the worshippers were true to God's Word.

If you are fortunate enough to be placed on an assignment by God or the Holy Spirit, you are amongst the blessed in the world. Only God knows your assignments and how He wants them executed. Being faithful and willing to respond when the Holy Spirit speaks to you are the key attributes you must have to receive this blessing.

My prophetess friend, Ms. Renay Goodman, prophesized to me that being on this assignment will take courage, strength, and strong faith. She told me that the devil will be incredibly angry and will attack my mind, body, and soul. Eventually, she said, "It will have you believe that it was a mistake believing that you could accomplish what God wants you to do." Talk about being terrified! What was the relevance of this assignment? "This is of God, not me," I told her. "I have no idea what this book will entail. I'm just following the will of God. I am just a messenger of Christ. Only the Holy Spirit who is guiding my thoughts and fingers knows. I am just being a vessel and a testament of His Word." Through John 14:17 (NIV), the Holy Spirit said to me, "But you know Him, for He lives with you and will be in you."

Being led by the Holy Spirit, I have had many dreams, seen visions, and heard the whispers of God, leading me to write what He wanted the world to hear in His book. In the book of Joel, you will find many prophesies about God speaking to His people. He tells us in Joel 2:28: "And it shall come to pass afterwards, that I will pour out my spirit upon all flesh; and your sons and your daughters shall prophesy, your old men shall dream dreams, your young men shall see visions."

With the prophecy being yielded despite the attacks of Satan, I noticed in January 2020 that my hair was starting to weaken and break off from a new product I had purchased online. I discontinued to use it and threw it away; however, the damage was already done. The prophecies from Ms. Goodman were already starting to take effect, and I had to be ready for what was next. Satan had begun his attacks upon me. However, I knew ahead of time that God was getting ready to use me mightily, and Satan wanted to get a head start to deter my mind. Always aiming to be faddish with my hair and my face, seeing the attack upon them frightened me.

My hair, at its strongest, normally was a few inches past my shoulders. However, with the attach from Satan, it was approximately an inch above my eyebrows. I was devastated. My beautiful hair had been destroyed. In 2014, I listened to a coworker about getting my hair colored and decided to go to a local salon at the mall in Augusta, Georgia. What a huge mistake! It was the wrong day for hair coloring. A lady was having a seizure, and all the beauticians to include mine, attended to her. They completely forgot that they had other customers. The color stayed in my hair for nearly an hour, and the damage was done. Unbeknownst to me, two weeks later, while washing my hair at home, most of my hair fell out. I used the same product I had always used to wash my hair. But that day, Satan had other plans. He attacked my hair, and he attacked my mind. I could not stop the tears.

Subconsciously, the devil had me thinking that I had developed breast cancer or even brain cancer. I was terrified. I started to feel ugly, and my self-esteem started to dwindle. My faith was diminishing. *How could such a thing happen to me again?* I thought while looking in the mirror with tears in my eyes. Though my husband tried to comfort me and tell me that my hair would grow back, it was not what I wanted to hear. How could God allow this to happen to His own child?

Then, I thought about Jesus laying down His life for us and the pain He suffered before returning to glory. Losing hair was nothing compared to what He had to go through. Somehow, God laid on my heart the words in James 4:7, "Submit yourselves therefore to God. Resist the devil, and he will flee from you." I held my head up and kept praising God. You see, when we give God the glory, Satan gets mad and starts his attacks. But we have to stand strong on the Word of God and tell Satan to get behind us. He does not belong in our lives.

I began to feel like Jesus in the desert being tempted by Satan and how Jesus resisted Satan and, eventually, he fled from Jesus. When I realized Satan was not finished with me and wanted to really test my faith in the Lord, I had to pray consistently. He attacked something he knew would bring me to tears—my face. Being a sufferer of low self-esteem, I always thought the only two things I had going for me were my hair and my face. It never occurred to me that I had the Word of God and Jesus on my side. Howbeit, in mid-February 2020, Satan attacked my face with a horrible rash. I could not hold back the tears streaming down my face. As I gazed upon myself in the mirror, I saw a woman of God that once was blessed with beautiful hair and skin crumbling and falling into pieces. But little did I know, these material things that we treasure on earth will soon fade away. We put things like beauty, houses, and cars before God. We must submit ourselves before God, and He will take care of the rest.

When Sunday fell upon me, I went to church and stood up. I stood boldly testifying to what was going on with me. As I stood there testifying about the greatness of God, something got a hold of me. I started to scream, and I told Satan, "You cannot and will not have my body, face, and you do not have my mind. I am beautiful, and I am a child of the Highest God." A load, it seemed, fell from my shoulders that day because I was able to stand strong on the Word of God. Telling Satan to flee relieved years of stress from my mind. I held my head up high and walked away as the parishioners stood to their feet, applauding me. Satan thought he had control of my mind, but God took control of my heart.

When we rebuke the devil, he will flee from us. We must stand strong in this fight that we are up against. And we must prepare ourselves for what is coming. It will not be pretty, but those of faith will survive and be taken to the great tabernacle of the Lord.

CHAPTER 1: WHAT IS A CHERUBIM?

Angels of protection are all around you.

In Genesis 3:24, we find these words: "So he drove out the man; and he placed at the east of the garden of Eden Cherubims and a flaming sword which turned every way, to keep the way of the tree of life."

On March 25, 2020, the Holy Spirit asked, "Do you know what a Cherubim is?" The only thing.

I could think of at the time was the Scripture in Psalm 1:4, "The ungodly are not so: but are like the chaff which the wind driveth away." We recited this Scripture so much at the AME church when I was a teenager that chaff, not cherubim, immediately came to mind.

But I quickly realized these were two totally different things. A *chaff* is the husks of corn or other seeds separated by threshing. As described in biblical tradition, a *cherubim* is an order of unearthly, angelic winged beings that attend to God. These angels resemble a person. A cherubim was assigned to protect the entrance to the Garden of Eden.

Ezekiel 1:4-28 and Ezekiel 10: 3-22. God placed a cherubim and a flaming sword at the Garden of Eden to guard the way to the entrance of the tree of life. Reading the entire verses will help you understand what God intends in the Scriptures. God put His seal of protection around us when He placed the cherubim at the gates. God wants us to believe that He will always protect us no matter what man puts in our paths. God does not want us to fear what we can see but to fear Him, which we cannot see. By placing a cherubim at our gates, He will protect us from the things that we can see.

I could not understand why the Holy Spirit was asking me what a cherubim was or where He was leading me. However, on Palm Sunday 2020, it changed my life forever. Many do not believe in Christ, the Holy Spirit, or God, but they will discover that only God will save them from all unrighteousness and their sins.

CHAPTER 2: THE GREAT REVIVAL

Hebrews 9:1-2 New International Version (NIV): "Now the first covenant had regulations for worship and also an earthly sanctuary. A tabernacle was set up. In its first room were the lampstand and the table with its consecrated bread; this was called the Holy Place."

Since 2017, the pastors at the River of Life Worship Center had been praying for a revival. Traditionally, many institutions conduct revivals during the spring and fall; however, unless a revival is called by God, it is not conducted at the River of Life Worship Center for monetary gain or as a biannual ritual. The center focuses on revival through prayer and hearing the Word of God. While waiting for a ritual to be called by God, our head pastor indicated that, in the coming days, many people would be walking up the streets, standing in the parking lot, and gathering at windows trying to receive the Word of God. She also indicated that church as we knew it would never be the same. And what a change it has been!

Consequently, in March 2020, church, as we all knew it, was no longer. In fact, many states' ordinances declared that there would be no more than ten people assembling in the house of worship or could gather in the sanctuary at one time. Worship had to be conducted either online or while social distancing. This was heartbreaking for so many people of Christ, especially me.

A virus that many blamed on China had come, and the entire world would experience its punishment. However, this virus had nothing to do with China. This was from God and, until Christians realize and understand that God is in control of this virus, the world will *never* heal. Though China may be responsible for many things in life, China cannot shut down the entire world at one time—only God can make that happen.

God, with His tremendous power, looked upon the earth just like He did in Genesis 6:5-6,

> And God saw that the wickedness of man was great in
> the earth, and that every imagination of the thoughts
> of his heart was only evil continually. And it repented
> the Lord that He had made man on the earth and it

grieved Him at His heart.

God is saying to us, "No more! Wake up, people!" This virus has nothing to do with China or mankind. This coronavirus is a God-thing cast upon the earth. It is one of many plagues that are to come. When God allowed the plague of locusts to attack the Middle East and Africa in December 2019, He was trying to show the world that His prophecies from Exodus and Revelation were coming to pass.

God is doing the same thing now. It is no accident that the world is in turmoil with fires in California, Washington, and the surrounding areas. Floods, hurricanes, and tornadoes are flourishing in the Midwest, the south, and even the east coast. The coronavirus is shutting down the entire world to include casinos, sports arenas, concerts, and entertainment centers. Even the church is shut down because of the greed and molestations taking place with religious leaders. God created this virus so that His great revival could take place. God needed the world to stand still and take note of what is to come. He is showing His signs, and if you are not grounded by the Word of God, you will miss them and fall to your death. The Bible says in Romans 2:11-12: "For there is no respect of persons with God. For as many as have sinned without law shall also perish without law; and as many as have sinned in the law shall be judged by the law." It does not matter what color, denomination, or how rich or poor you are. God allows things to happen to show the world that He and only He is in control.

Throughout history, people have failed God, and He is tired of it. These plagues have been released upon the earth because of the sins of man. This revival that my pastor and many others are referring to is not like the typical revivals conducted once or twice yearly. This is a revival for repentance and the coming of Christ. God sent this *Great Revival,* so we could revive ourselves and come to Christ before it is too late.

2 Chronicles 7:14: "If my people who are called by my name, will humble themselves and pray and seek my face and turn from their wicked ways, then I will hear from Heaven and I will forgive their sin and will heal their land." God is sending a message to the world saying, "All men will bow down to Him." He clearly says it in Romans 14:11: "For it is written As I live, saith the Lord, every knee shall bow to me and every tongue shall confess to God." God wants the world to get our house in order. He is tired of murderers, liars, cheaters, rapists, adulterers, homosexuals, lesbians, transgender people, and

many more. This is not how God created His world. When God sent us to this world, we were to accomplish things on earth to show peace and love to our fellow man, woman, boy, and girl—not cause confusion and disruption. God wanted us to be focused on His business and not destroy what He created.

When man took upon himself to change what God created him to be, this angered God. He made you a man or woman. He did not give you a choice in the matter. Some may say that it's their choice to change how they want to be, but it's not how God created you. He created you in His image and not what you think you should be. I believe in hearing from the Holy Spirit that this is the last straw with God. It angered Him so much to see that man had deceived Him once again. Man's greed in developing a way to capitalize by changing what God created has caused this world to stand still.

During this great revival of Christ, there will be trials, tribulations, hardship, and a lot of pain, suffering, and sorrow. God understands that. He wants to see how we respond to what He is doing. He is giving us a second chance to get it right. God is using this great revival as a test.

Man's greed failed God's expectations. We hear repeatedly, "Let's get the economy started back up, so people can go to work." That is not what God wants. He wants us to *listen* to what He is saying. Man is so worried about their jobs, the economy, and other things that they forgot about kneeling and praying to God.

God said, "Just ask, and I will give you the desires of your hearts." Man chose the wrong path on this. When States closed the house of worship and let them remain closed until the third phase that angered God even more. You do not open everything, especially Casinos, before opening God's place of worship! You keep the churches open so that man can fall down on their knees and worship God! This is God's revival! But man is too proud to humble himself before the Lord. Man is too concerned about what others will say. The people you are embarrassed to praise God or fall on your knees in front of will be the same people that follow you to your world of eternal damnation.

God has a chosen few that will be able to see things no other man or woman has seen during this great revival. I am blessed to be one of them. For instance, as you will read in chapter five of this book, God chose me to be able to see directly into the sun on March 22, 2020, and see things that only He wanted me to see. God knew that I would be a witness and would testify of His greatness. Furthermore, God will use many to minister to others that have never set foot in church before because of what has happened to them during this great revival. This is a time-out period that God has placed upon us. However, what is to come will cause a great cry upon the earth.

God wants us to be diligent. He wants us to bow down and worship Him and Him only.

Donna Hodges

CHAPTER 3: FOCUS ON THE WORD OF GOD

During this time of discretion, God wants us to remain focused on Him and His Word. No matter what the circumstances are, He wants us to remain focused. Sometimes it is exceedingly difficult to be focused on God or His Word because of the coronavirus and the impact it has on the world. At times, I find it awfully hard to focus on my pastor's word when she is delivering it via telephone because I cannot see her. At times, the sound will not be clear, or something else may distract me. I have to ask God for forgiveness because I am not focused on what she is saying.

Because of this, I have gotten discouraged and found myself doing other things that do not pertain to the Word of God. Take, for instance, the morning of May 24, 2020, as my pastor was teaching "Learning to Wait on God," I found myself distracted in many ways. Since we had to call in, other things caught my attention, and before I knew it, I was working on one of my novels. I felt so ashamed and wretched afterward.

But through all of this, God already knew how I would feel and had me go to my husband to receive comfort. God knows our thoughts and needs before we go to others for support. Here we find pointers on how we can remain focused on God's Word without going astray:

(1) **Read God's Word Daily**: David says in Psalm 119:105 (KJV) that "Thy word is a lamp unto my feet and a light unto my path." In order for us to be prosperous, we must be able to meditate on God's Word day and night. God's Word will train our brains to act according to what He has designed for our lives. His Word keeps us competent and equipped for all the good work we do.

(2) **Obey the Will of God**: Sometimes we may not know what God's will is for us, but we can listen to what He is trying to tell us. Being obedient unites us closer to God and transforms our minds so that His will is being done and not

the will of someone else.

(3) **Witness to Others**: When we deliver God's Word to others, He gains a new prospect into the kingdom of heaven. God did not put us on earth to party and have a good time. He put us here as disciples, so we can continue what Jesus started. When Jesus left this earth, He told His disciples to witness to His sheep and make disciples of them.

(4) **Stay Diligent to Him**: Proverbs 13:4 (ESV) says, "The soul of the sluggard craves and gets nothing, while the soul of the diligent is richly supplied." God wants us to put forth great effort in everything that we do while remaining faithful to Him.

(5) **Listen Attentively**: Since the summer of 2019, my right ear has been besieged with a loud staticky noise making it exceedingly difficult for me to hear clearly and stay focused. Although I have seen several ENT physicians and audiologists, the noise still persists in my ears. The condition, they call "TMJ—

Temporomandibular Joint Dysfunction," is a disturbance I wish to go away. Trying to listen attentively to the Word of God is nearly impossible for me at times. Though I have prayed and trusted God for deliverance, it is always on His time when He chooses to deliver us.

CHAPTER 4: CATECHISM

Revelation 22:7: "Behold, I come quickly; blessed is he that keepeth the sayings of the prophecy of this book."

On September 26, 2020, I dreamt that I was asking God a series of questions. One, in particular was, "When? When will I be releasing this assignment to the world? And, through what avenue will it be distributed?" Feeling a slight pain in my head and my ears, I slowly began to wake up. Touching my forehead, I began rebuking the devil. I told him that God had already delivered me from migraine headaches, and I refuse to take them back.

Noticing that the common denominator between my headaches and the loud noise in my ears was the medication I had been prescribed, I asked the Lord to remove the symptoms from me. I did not want to be dependent upon something I did not need. What many people fail to realize is that the medications prescribed by doctors have several side effects. What may work for migraines can cause ailments in another part of your body. However, the only way to get relief is to take another form of medication.

As I began speaking to the Holy Spirit, I kept hearing the songs "We Are Standing on Holy Ground" and "Thank You, Lord" by Walter Hawkins. Then, the Holy Spirit said unto me as I lay upon my pillow, "You know, I can wipe the entire world out while you sleep, drive, fly, or doing whatever you are doing, and no one would know what hit them?"

That caught my attention! Trying to grasp what the Holy Spirit was saying, deep inside, I knew He was saying it for a reason. Whatever we are doing, do it to the best of His ability and not ours! God is the one that causes us to rise in the morning and lay down at night. He could put a stop to all of this in the twinkling of an eye. I believe that is what He was telling me.

God wants us to do is wake up! Stop lounging around like the world does not exist. Do things for His Glory! So, I got up and went into my living room. Since it was early on a Saturday morning, I figured I would lay down a little while longer on the couch, but God already knew my thoughts before

I came into the room.

I asked the Holy Spirit as I laid down again, "When will I hear from you in reference to my assignment?" Not realizing that this is how I got into the situation in the first place, I heard the word "*Catechism.*"

I was like Catechism, "What's that?" I never heard that word before in my life. I picked up my cell phone and spoke the word into the microphone, and the definition blew me away: "A summary of the principles of Christian religion in the form of questions and answers used for instructions of Christians."

Wait! Is that what I have been asking God about that morning? It began in the form of questioning, and now He has given me a word that I have never heard before.

As Christians, we question God daily, although we can get answers from His Word. Sometimes, God will reply right away, but, most times, He wants us to read and study His Word so that we can find the answers to our questions.

Out of curiosity, I wanted to dig deeper into this word *Catechism*, so I googled: "Where can I find Catechism in the Bible?" This is where it got serious. The search returned Revelation 22:18-19,

For I testify unto every man that heareth the words of the prophecy of this book. If any man shall add unto these things, God shall add unto him the plagues that are written in this book. And if any man shall take away from the words of the book of this prophecy, God shall take away his part out of the book of life, and out of the holy city, and from the things which are written in this book.

Man has changed the original words of the Bible to their satisfaction and understanding. By doing so, it allows them to capitalize on the Word of God. My suggestion to you is to read Revelation 22:18-19 over and over again until you are able to understand what God means by this. "Stop trying to profit off God's word and find an understanding to what is already written," says the Holy Spirit.

CHAPTER 5: SEEING THROUGH THE SUN

God's Revelations:

Acts 2:19-20: "And I will show wonders in heaven above, and signs in the earth beneath; blood, and fire, and vapor of smoke; The sun shall be turned into darkness, and the moon into blood, before that great and notable day of the Lord."

By the time March 22, 2020, rolled around, the world was at a complete standstill. People were dying all around us. Man could not go to work, nor could they go outside without a mask. Entertainment centers and arenas had closed their doors to concerts, basketball, and football. Theatres and even restaurants had to shut their doors because of the rapidly spreading growth of the coronavirus. But the worst of them all was the closure of churches and temples of God. No one could worship in the presence of God due to a virus that has shut down the entire world—the coronavirus. The plagues of the Bible are slowly coming to pass, and no one is exempt from its fury nor the wrath of God. Only congregations of ten or less could enter the house of worship and obtain the Word of God. This outbreak of the coronavirus has had a devastating effect on our communities, churches, cities, states, nations, and the world. Many have been quarantined, and many lives have been lost.

The fear of dying has fallen upon so many. Yet, the church where I worship and many others have kept their doors open for those that are faithful, believe, and trust God for spiritual deliverance and guidance. Small Prayer Services with no more than ten people commenced on Sunday mornings. Many that could not enter joined on the outside, walking the streets and fields praising the name of Jesus. Howbeit, on Sunday morning, March 22, 2020, the Holy Spirit told me to get dress and start attending these services. As I drove through the wooded area trying to reach Redmiles Lane in Odenton, Maryland, I was met by one of the deaconesses. Rolling down my window to greet her, she informed me that too many people were already at the service and that they were turning members away. Thanking her in advance for the heads-up, I said, "I guess I will turn around as well." Now, just because she was turned away did not mean that God was going to allow them to turn me away also.

Continuing my drive towards the church, the Holy Spirit said to me, "Keep Going." Being faithful and obedient to the Holy Spirit, I kept going until I saw a rare sight at my church—only a handful of cars. Sadness overcame my face as I had never seen a Sunday at the River of Life Worship Center without a packed parking lot. Parishioners were hungry for the Word of God and would rush to fill the lot every Sunday. But this Sunday, it was empty and lonely. Parishioners wanted to adhere to what man had told them, "Stay home!" But not me! I was not going to let man control what God had already established in place for me.

As I pulled up to the parking area, I was greeted by two deacons who told me likewise—there was no room for me. But you see, when God is in the mix, and you are faithful to Him, He will make a way out of no way. I told them, "I have come to pay my tithes and offerings. Can you take it in for me?"

At that point, one of the deacons looked at me and said, "Sister Donna, there is actually one more space in the church for someone if you would like to attend."

But God! I thought to myself as I smiled. *That's a blessing! I really need the prayer time this morning. So much is on my mind, and I need to see and feel the presence of the Holy Spirit,* I responded to him.

I stepped out of my car and entered through the double glass doors remembering Psalm 91:1: "He that dwelleth in the secret place of the most High shall abide under the shadow of the Almighty." The glory of the Lord had already filled the building. I placed my Bible and my jacket on the pew where I normally sat and began to worship with the other parishioners.

As the spirit of the Lord came upon me, a handful of saints were already pacing the aisles, praying and speaking in tongues. I smiled thinking about Acts 2:1: "And when the day of Pentecost was fully come, they were all with one accord in one place." Consumed by the Holy Spirit, I began praying to God and seeking the Holy Spirit.

On the inside of our church, just above the planted garden, is a beautifully stained glass with many shades. On the inside of the stained glass are a cross, a dove, and a circle. The Holy Spirit first alerted my eyes towards the stained glass one Sunday in March 2018 while praise and worship were commencing. At that point, the Holy Spirit encountered my body and told me to close my eyes. The image that I saw next nearly brought me to my knees. The Holy Spirit was revealing Himself to me. I was so overcome with tongues and the power of the Holy Ghost that I ran to the front of the church praising God. In my mind, no one else was there but me and the Holy Spirit dwelling within my soul.

But, the morning of March 22, 2020, at 09:43 a.m., when the Holy Spirit revealed Himself to me, darkness fell behind Him. I immediately opened my eyes because I did not want to see what the Holy Spirit was trying to show me. I knew it was not going to be good. Most of the times when the Holy Spirit revealed Himself to me, it had been a warning about something drastic happening in the world or in my family. On January 27, 2020, the Holy Spirit revealed Himself to me and, behind Him, I saw a figure and total darkness. I went home from church and told my husband about it. I told him, "Whatever it is, honey, it's going to be very bad." He looked at me in amazement. A couple of hours later, my husband said a news flash came on the TV that NBA Star Kobe Bryant and several others had crashed into a mountain. There were no survivors. I was devastated.

By March 22, 2020, at 09:43 a.m., the coronavirus had taken the lives of nearly ten Americans. When the Holy Spirit revealed Himself to me and showed me complete darkness, I stood in place and pleaded with Him to deliver us from this virus. When I had finished, most of the people that had come in to pray during the time I had come were gone. Another group had taken their place to include our pastor.

I gathered my things and left the church, heading towards my car. Others had gathered outside, walking, praising, and praying. I had a weird feeling as I opened my car door. And when I sat down to start my car, I felt guilty about leaving without joining the group. As I pulled out of the parking space, the Holy Spirit instructed me to pull into another space close to a lamp post near an open field. I obeyed the Holy Spirit. Then the Holy Spirit spoke to me and said, "Get out and go into the field." I was afraid. All I could think about was Matthew 24:40: "Two men were in the field; one will be taken and the other left behind" and Matthew 24:42: "Watch therefore, for you do not know the hour your Lord is coming."

However, I had to be obedient to the Holy Spirit. I did not know what to expect, but I went into the field as directed, facing the front of our church. Immediately, I began walking around and praying to God in the Spirit. I did not know what came over me but, suddenly, it was as if someone grabbed hold of my hands and pulled them towards the sky. I felt like Jesus, hanging on the cross. I was keenly aware of everything that was taking place in my mind, like Moses when he was on the mountaintop. With outstretched arms and hands, I gazed into the sky, noticing white streaks left behind from airplanes. The sky was clear. It had beautiful light blue peaks stretching from one end of the earth to the other. As I beheld His greatness, my eyes turned towards the front of the church, where the sun was facing directly at me. His brightness shined down upon me, swallowing me into His presence. The beams reigned down from every direction. The fullness of the Lord took control.

Casting my eyes upon His greatness, I was afraid at first but, as I was going around in circles, I felt a great calmness in my spirit. I heard a voice from the Holy Spirit as He guided my eyes towards Him, saying, "Look up. Be not afraid, for I am with you." I wanted to fall down on my knees and worship Him, but He would not allow me because of the tongues that flowed so beautifully from my mouth. The Holy Spirit had given me a new set of tongues as I spoke to Him. And though

I was always told not to look into the sun as a child because I might go blind or have severe eye damage, I trusted God because He said in Deuteronomy 31:6: "Be strong and of a good courage, fear not, nor be afraid of them: for the Lord thy God, he it is that doth go with thee: he will not fail thee nor forsake thee."

With my eyes beholding the sun and my arms stretched wide, I was able to see straight into it. I mean—it was the greatest vision God had ever given me. I saw everything. I could see the glow from a sharp, shiny bright light beaming from top to bottom. It was a crystal-clear sword coming down into rectangular points on every side, forming the shape of a cross. The beauty and clearness of it alone could blind you. *If only there was a snapshot of it on my camera,* I thought. *Who would believe such a thing?* It is impossible to try and describe it. There were two figures in long black cloth-like robes on the right side of the sun. Their faces were covered. I could not make them out.

I did not believe what God was revealing to me, and I wanted so badly to adjust my eyes, but He would not let me. In the fullness of His holiness, He wanted me to stay focused. It was on His time and His time only that I could remove my eyes, not mine. After a few moments of captivation, the Holy Spirit removed my eyes so I could see His glory in the sky and all around me. I started to see large blobs of yellow in the sky everywhere my eyes laid.

At first, I thought I was losing my sight, but the Holy Spirit said to me, "These are angels that I have placed upon the earth to watch over you." I was in awe because on Wednesday, March 18, 2020, around 8:40 a.m., a coworker named Prophetess Renay Goodman had just told me those exact words as she handed me her Bible and told me to read Psalm 91. Although I could not take her Bible at that time, I asked her to meet me in the cafeteria at 11:00 a.m., and I would retrieve it then. She asked me to keep it and read it but, that Friday, March 20, 2020, the Holy Spirit instructed me to give the Bible back to her because she would be needing it.

Furthermore, when my eyes were able to see clearly, the Spirit of the Lord came upon me so that I could pray in the Spirit. First, I prayed softly. Then, as the Spirit dwelled in me, I started praying heavily. The people that were walking around the parking began to come near to see what was going on. One of the deacons came towards his truck that was parked directly in front of me. He got inside and let down his window, so he could hear and see what I was doing. I could feel others coming closer towards me, but I was so engulfed in the Spirit that I could only sense their presence. God was making witnesses out of them. As I continued to look into the sun, it opened up, and a bright yellow glowing light appeared on the inside. My tongues went deeper into another form that I had never heard come from my mouth. A long beam came down from the sun, and the Holy Spirit showed me figures. I don't know if they were angels or what they were. But I could see images pouring out of the sun. I continued to pray—crying and worshipping the Lord God Almighty.

Suddenly, I saw a bright shining bronze altar with three long poles coming down on each side and in the middle. Then, the Holy Spirit said, "Remove your eyes and look upon the earth again!" I slowly walked in circles, and I could see more lines from airplanes that had passed by. I heard the sound of black birds squawking near me, but I did not know what direction they were coming from. Then, the Holy Spirit had me turn around, and I saw one black bird fly away, and a big airplane fly to my right. A big bright yellow light came immediately after they passed by.

This sequence of events took place for roughly thirty

minutes in the field of my church, River of Life Worship Center in Odenton, Maryland, as I stood there praying in the Spirit with many different tongues facing the sky. The Holy Spirit again said, "These are the angels that I have placed to guard you." But my eyes could not see anything but the yellow blobs as He pulled my eyes away from the earth and showed me the sun for the final time. Just as clear as day, I was able to look into the sun again, but, this time, He revealed total darkness. The sun turned into a dark black circle with a ring around it. However, it did not last long, maybe twenty seconds or so. I did not try to count. My mind was overtaken by the joy of seeing through the sun. Then, the bright yellow light or glow came back with a long beam. I do not know if they were angels or what, but I could see figures just popping out of the sun, and I continued to pray with tears streaming down my face. All of a sudden, I saw the two figures and the altar again before God removed my eyes for the final time.

As I beheld His glory in that field, I started to cry harder. I praised God for quite some time, thanking Him for all that He had given me, for what He had done in my life, for deliverance, and all the revelations He has shown me through the sun—the power of the Holy Spirit, the angels in the sky, the altar, the two figures, the cross, and the sword. What did I do to deserve His greatness like this? I thanked God for allowing His angels to watch over me and my family my entire life and especially for salvation.

Then, the Holy Spirit said, "Look over at the marquee in the field!" I could see it plain as day without my glasses. Regretfully, I had never paid attention to our marquee before. I just knew that I could not see it from afar without my eyeglasses. As I gazed upon our marquee, it read, "'See, I am doing a new thing! Now it springs up' Isaiah 43:19." The Holy Spirit said, "I told you that you would not lose your sight." He already knew what was going to happen to me and had these words to be a testament to what I had seen. It was then I realized that God had me on an assignment. I had to be a witness to the things He was showing me because He was preparing me for what was to come.

I was instructed by the Holy Spirit to get into my car and drive away. I was not to look upon anyone until I reached my house. He told me to go home and document the events as they happened. When I got into my car, I tried placing my glasses on my face to adjust my vision but was quickly scolded by the Holy Spirit, "Did I not just prove to you that you could see without your glasses?" I removed them from my face and drove away. Everywhere I looked, I saw bright yellow spots. I was so afraid that I was going to lose my vision, but the Holy Spirit asked me, "Where is your faith, Donna?" Again, that was my confirmation that the Spirit dwells in me. I started rejoicing in my car. Tears were streaming down my cheeks. *Did this really just happen to me? But how? Why me?*

As I turned down the road leading to our cul-de-sac, it all made sense. God had been using me my entire life, but I was too busy doing other things to pay attention to my gifts until that day, March 22, 2020. When I pulled into my driveway, bright yellow lights beamed everywhere. I saw them in the trees, the sky, on cars, on houses—everywhere I looked.

As I approached my door, I turned once again, trying to get a glimpse of the sun, but it was too bright, and it hurt my eyes. I could not even bear to look at any of the rays beaming down upon me. I could not understand how I was able to look clearly into the sun at my church but, when I got home, I could not bear to look at it. How was that even possible? Then I heard the Holy Spirit say, "Only when I have you look upon the sun, you will see, and you will know." I left it alone.

I gathered all my things and ran into the house. Instead

of obeying the Holy Spirit and documenting what I saw, I went downstairs into the basement where my husband was and started to tell him what happened. I was so overcome with joy that I pulled out my cell phone and started talking into it as I told him the vision from the sun. I mean—how could God use me like that to see His glory? Was I even worthy?

CHAPTER 6: LAYING DOWN HIS LIFE

Greater love hath no man than this, that a man lay down his life for his friends. Ye are my friends, if ye do whatsoever I command you; henceforth, I call you not servants, for the servant knoweth not what his lord doeth; but I have called you friends.

John 15:13-15

Jesus is that friend that has laid down His life for all mankind. When the glory of the Lord fell upon me, my life changed forever. I especially felt this change after telling my husband Terry about the friend that laid down His life for us. Though Christ had been a part of my life since I was a child, seeing Him through the sun was a phenomenon I will never forget. Given what the Holy Spirit had just shown me, I headed upstairs to document what I had seen. I went into the kitchen first to retrieve something to drink but, as I looked out the window, I realized the Holy Spirit was not finished with me yet. I could not believe my eyes. A big white "X" was in the sky to the right of my house. I grabbed my cell phone to take a picture. I knew this was indeed something I could behold and tell others about.

I opened the front door, and it was still there, just as plain as day. I was not seeing things. There was indeed a big "X" in the sky. But when I attempted to take the picture with my cellphone, I could not see it through the lens. It was pitch black. But the Holy Spirit whispered in my ears and said, "Just point your camera, and it will be there." As usual, I obeyed the Holy Spirit, and when I looked at the picture in front of me, the picture was there. The same big X that I had seen from the kitchen window.

I ran downstairs again to tell my husband, realizing that I still had not documented the previous events. The Holy Spirit really was using me as a witness for my husband that day. This time, my husband followed me to the opened door and saw exactly what I had seen. We went back downstairs to discuss what we had just seen. Knowing that God had me on an assignment that needed to be fulfilled, I told him that

I needed to go back upstairs to document the events that the Holy Spirit had revealed to me.

Instead, I headed to the door to see if the X was still there. To my amazement, when I looked out the door, and the "X" had moved closer to the sun. I could not bear to look upon it. My eyes had started to hurt from earlier, and the glare was just too bright. Again, I pointed my camera towards it and took the picture. There it was just as beautiful as ever. But the "X" was no longer an "X"—it had turned sideways. I heard the voice of the Lord say, "I canceled your sins when I laid down my life for you."

I dashed back into the house, showing my husband the pictures I had just taken. Could this truly be happening to me? My husband and I went into a deep discussion about what this all meant. It was God using me to witness to my husband, my son, and the world about God's goodness.

The "X" in the sky.

The sun I was able to look upon on March 22, 2020.

CHAPTER 7: PROPHECY OF THE SUN

I will raise them up a Prophet from among their
brethren, like unto thee, and will put my words in
his mouth; and he shall speak unto them all that I
shall command him. And it shall come to pass, that
whosoever will not hearken unto my words which he
shall speak in my name, I will require it of him.

Deuteronomy 18:18-19

On March 27, 2020, at 10:41 p.m., my phone rang.
Being that it was after 10:00 p.m., I immediately thought, *This
cannot be good.* I looked at the number, and I knew it was
someone in Maryland. The only two people that would dare
call me so late at night were my best friend, Prophetess Pamela
Hunter, or my new friend, Prophetess Renay Goodman. Seeing
that it was Prophetess Renay, I got excited because I wanted to

share with her what had happened to me on Sunday, March 22, 2020, after prayer service.

"Hello," I answered the phone with anticipation.

"Hello, Donna. This is Ms. Renay. I wanted to tell you that I have my Bible. It was in my bag downstairs."

"That's great!" I said. Then, immediately went into what the Holy Spirit led me to share with her. "Ms. Renay, do you remember me telling you that the Holy Spirit had me bring your Bible back to you because He said that you would need it?"

"Yes, and I am glad that you did. A friend of mine got caught up in some things, and I needed this particular Bible to tell him about the translation of what he asked."

The conversation went on for a while as we discussed many things. Then, I told Ms. Renay, "I am so glad you called me because there is something I need to tell you, and when I tell you this, it will blow your mind." I could sense her listening with anticipation because she got very quiet.

"Our church has Prayer Service on Sunday even though there were only ten people allowed in the building," I told her.

"Yes. Go ahead," she said.

"I got a chance to go inside after one of the deacons

decided to let me take his spot. I was so thrilled because the lady before me was turned around, but I guess they knew the Lord wanted me inside."

"We didn't even have service. We were told to stay home," she replied with a little anxiety.

"Well, they allowed me to go in, and when I did, the Holy Spirit was all over that place. I could see the parishioners walking up and down the aisles praising the Lord as the prayer leader was praying in the Spirit. I put my things down and started to do likewise. At that point, the Holy Spirit embraced my mind, my heart, and placed my eyes at the top of the church where a glass-stained windowpane has helped me to see the Holy Spirit since May 2018."

"Uh-hmm," she said, waiting for me to finish what I was trying to tell her.

"It was at that point that I looked around and discovered that none of the people that originally started out with me were still in the church. A new group had entered. So, I picked up my things, noticing that our pastor had also arrived and joined in on the service."

"Did you go back home?" Ms. Renay asked in suspense.

"No, ma'am. I walked out of the building, noticing that

several of the church members were upon the grounds of the church praying. I felt kind of strange getting back into my car and driving off. But when I got in to drive away, the Holy Spirit boldly said, 'Pull there!' It was the first parking space as you entered the church grounds near a tall silver pole. Then, the Holy Spirit said, 'Get out and go into the field.'"

The phone was quiet. You could hear a pin drop as Ms. Renay listened without interrupting me. If she had been telling me this story, I probably would have interrupted several times. I can be very restless and eager to speak when someone else is talking.

"Did you go into the field?" She asked.

"Yes, ma'am, I did." My voice started to tremble. "Ms. Renay, the Holy Spirit spoke to me and said, 'Look up towards the sky!'"

After telling the sequence of events that took place in the field, she began to prophesize on what this really meant to me.

Sister Renay told me the Holy Spirit wanted me to lay upon my face and pray for healing of the land and the earth. She told me that the cross I had seen in the sun was preparing me to see things in the natural. I had been chosen by God to see these things, and it behooves me to lay on my face and ask God to reveal these things to me. She said, "God chose you because you could hear and see what He had for you. And, you would be obedient to his hearing."

Then Sister Renay said, "The Sword you saw was the 'Sword of God' from the Scripture, Hebrews 4:12: 'For the Word of God is quick, and powerful and sharper than a two-edged sword, piercing even to the dividing asunder of soul and spirit, and of the joints and marrow and is a discerner of the thoughts and intents of the heart.' It cuts sin and heals. It cuts into your heart and heals the heart. The cross was Jesus laying to the side. He laid down His life for us. The Spirit of the Holy Ghost guides your tongue. The Holy Ghost reveals secrets that you may not even know you have uttered."

Donna Hodges

CHAPTER 8: ARK OF THE COVENANT

And after the second veil, the tabernacle which is called the Holiest of all; Which had the golden censer, and the ark of the covenant overlaid roundabout with gold, wherein was the golden pot that had manna, and Aaron's rod that budded, and the tables of the covenant; And over it the Cherubim of glory shadowing the mercy seat; of which we cannot now speak particularly.

Hebrews 9:3-5

According to the book of Exodus, Moses had the Ark of the Covenant built to hold the Ten Commandments at the command of God. Throughout the years, the Ark had traveled with the Israelites during their forty-year quest in the desert to Shiloh. However, King David took the Ark to Jerusalem, where Solomon, his son, had it installed in the temple. In 586 BC (Before Christ), the Ark disappeared for over 2,000 years, and was said that Levitical Priests moved the Ark to Egypt just before Babylon sacked Jerusalem.

Currently, the Ark resides in Ethiopia in a place called Aksum in the St. Mary of Zion Cathedral. The apostle John wrote in the book of Hebrews 9:4 that the Ark of the Covenant contained three things:

1. The golden pot that held manna,

2. Aaron's rod, and

3. The tablets of the covenant.

"And the temple of God was opened in heaven, and there was seen in his temple the ark of his testament: and there was lightnings, and voices, and thundering, and an earthquake, and great hail" (Revelation 11:19).

As the end of the world is nearing, God is revealing to mankind the prophecies that were established while Jesus was on earth.

Oftentimes, the Bible speaks about the manna falling from the sky or bread that God used to feed his children. Manna was a comestible element provided by God to the Israelites while they traveled in the desert for forty years. I believe God is saying that if we are committed to Him and His Word, He will forever feed us with manna from heaven.

Aaron's rod represented the spiritual authority. Numbers 17:8 says, "And it came to pass, that on the morrow Moses went into the tabernacle of witness; and, behold, the rod of Aaron for the house of Levi was budded, and brought forth buds, and bloomed blossoms, and yielded almonds." Truly, the verse in Numbers is for such a time as this.

Donna Hodges

CHAPTER 9: SHORT OF GOD'S GLORY

Romans 3:23: "For all have sinned and come short of the glory of God."

God did not decree that some people have fallen short of His glory, but He declared that all had sinned and fallen short of His glory. God has no respect of person. When God looked for a righteous person, He could not find one. No, not one righteous person amongst many. All men and women were sinners.

Imagine! Standing before God and Him looking into your eyes, saying, "Flee from me, you worker of iniquity, I know you not." No, that is not what we want to hear as Christians. We want God's love and affection. We want to stand bold for the Lord and hear Him say, "Well done, thy good and faithful servant; thou hast been faithful over a few things, I will make thee ruler over many things. Enter thou into the joy of the Lord," as it says in Matthew 25:21.

From the very beginning, when God created man, man has fallen short of God's glory. Man defied God. God did not defy man. God told Adam not to eat of a certain tree, but Adam, being a man and listening to what a woman said instead of God, disobeyed God by eating the fruit from the tree of the knowledge of good and evil. For this reason, man fell short of God's glory and was cast out of the Garden of Eden. Can you imagine having everything you ever wanted in life and because you were disobedient to what God asked you to do, seeing it all taken away? Our God is a jealous God. He will have no other god or man before Him. We must listen to what God tells us to do. But, as humans, we choose to listen to everyone but God. We always do things our way.

However, when we have the favor of God and acknowledge Him, we do not have to worry about falling short of His glory because God will protect us in everything that is cast upon us. Take, for instance, the three Hebrew men who were set over the affairs of Babylon—Shadrach, Meshach, and Abednego. Because they chose not to fall down and worship the idol gods or graven images that King Nebuchadnezzar had built, in his rage and fury, he ordered that they be brought to him. He wanted to know if indeed it was true that they would not fall down and worship the golden image which he had set up? (Daniel 3:13-14).

They answered the king, "We are not careful to answer thee in this matter. If it be so, our God whom we serve is able to deliver us from the burning fiery furnace and he will deliver us out of thine hand, oh king," (Daniel 3:16-17). They were letting the king know that they would not serve false gods or worship his golden images, so the king cast them into a fiery furnace. Unbeknownst to the king, God was with Shadrach, Meshach, and Abednego that day and always. They stood up for God, and God was standing in the gap for them. By them letting the king know that they would serve no other gods but the God in heaven, God favored them and protected them. He did not let anything harmful come to them as God stood in the fiery furnace with them.

When King Nebuchadnezzar asked the question, "Did not we cast three men bound into the midst of the fire?" His counselors answered, "True, O king. Lo, I see four men loose, walking in the midst of the fire, and they have no hurt, and the form of the fourth is like the Son of God" (Daniel 3:24-25). God was in the midst of their situation. He already knew what was going to happen. They just had to be obedient and acknowledge God for who He is.

Having seen God's glory, the King of Babylon Nebuchadnezzar acknowledged God for Himself and decreed that,

> Every person, nation, and language, which spoke anything against the God of Shadrach, Meshach, and Abednego, shall be cut in pieces, and their houses shall be made a dunghill; because there is no other God that can deliver after this sort.

Daniel 3:29

Later, King Nebuchadnezzar had a dream and sought an interpretation from all the wise men and magicians in the land. As he told the dream, no one could interpret the dream. But when Daniel, who was called Belteshazzar, came into the room and was told the dream by the king, Daniel interpreted the dream saying,

> Therefore, O king, let my counsel be acceptable to you; break off his sins of righteousness and his iniquities by showing mercy to the poor that it may lengthen his tranquillity, the king spoke and said, "Is not this great Babylon, that I have built for the house of the kingdom by the might of my power, and for the

honour of my majesty?"

Daniel 4:27-30 (NKJV)

You see, although King Nebuchadnezzar had decreed that all men serve and worship God Almighty, he had become selfish in his own ways. The glory of the Lord was not upon him.

Consequently, when Daniel told him what thus saith the Lord, he knew that Daniel had heard from God. But as the words left King Nebuchadnezzar's mouth, a voice came from heaven and saying unto him, "O King Nebuchadnezzar, to thee it is spoken. The kingdom is departed from thee" (Daniel 4:31). The voice told King Nebuchadnezzar all that would happen to him had been interpreted from Daniel in his dream, and after the dream was fulfilled, everything the king had lost would be restored to him. At that point, King Nebuchadnezzar praised, extolled, and honored the King of heaven, all whose works are truth, and his ways judgment; and those that walk in pride, he is able to abase (Daniel 4:36-37).

When we have God's glory, our light will shine wherever we go. Doing things our way will cause God not to trust us, and we lose His glory.

Donna Hodges

CHAPTER 10: HOW THE VISIONS BEGAN

Tent Revivals

Psalm 85:6: "Wilt thou not revive us again; that thy people may rejoice in thee?"

I received Christ at a young age. But the most memorable moments are the two below—one being at First Pentecostal Church in Pensacola, Florida. At the age of eight, a bus would pick us up from our Moreno Court neighborhood and take us to church. While adults worshipped in the sanctuary, the children attended children's church. One Sunday in particular, while I was attending children's church, we were shown a movie called *The Burning Hell*. This film was not intended for children, but that Sunday in 1974, Christianity was scared into my soul. I was so afraid by seeing the people standing around an open pit of fire that it literally led me to speak in tongues.

One of the children's church leaders even said, "I believe she has the Holy Ghost." That day changed my life forever.

Later, at the age of fifteen, while attending an outdoor "Tent Revival," which was mainly held down south near a street corner or in an open field, my eyes were opened even further to what the Holy Spirit was doing in my life. Our "Tent Revivals" began at 9:00 p.m. and would go on until the wee hours of the morning—sometimes lasting until 4:00 a.m. However, no one complained. Everyone would be so caught up in the spirit that time did not matter. It was led by Bishop Polk (deceased): rest her soul, a beautiful lady, and prophetess of God. Her smile radiated through the walls of the tent every time I attended. Her hair was long and silky, and she always wore a classy suit or a long black robe. At the end of each sermon, she would be drenched with sweat. Bishop Polk was a true messenger for Christ.

I remember one Friday night during Tent Revival, Bishop Polk called me to come to the front of the tent. Astonished and afraid of what her prophecy for me would be, I was obedient and made my way to the front of the tent. I stood in the center of the aisle facing her as she stared intently into my eyes. I knew that if God told her to call me forward, it had to be something good. Most people would receive a prophecy of money, relationship, death, or that God was getting ready to do a mighty thing for them. But when she looked into my eyes, she smiled and said, "Baby, I see you as a missionary."

"A missionary?" I had heard about the life of missionaries and did not think that is who I was going to be.

She replied, "Yes, but not the kind that goes into the jungles or other countries, but the kind that dream dreams and sees visions." Little did she know, they had already started. I had no idea missionaries were also dreamers, seers, and prophetesses. I just saw them in movies and thought they went out into the jungles and preached the Gospel of Jesus Christ.

I received what she had told me and went back to my seat. The Holy Spirit had been showing me visions all my life. It not only scared me but my mother as well. I had no idea what was happening to me. But one of my aunts, Mary Jones (deceased), soon discovered that I had been touched by the Blood of Jesus Christ and the Holy Spirit at a young age and would be a carrier of His Word.

My mother and my cousin had gone with me to the Tent Revival on Friday night. They had heard about the Holy Spirit overtaking my body and how I would shout all over the tent.

They wanted to come and see for themselves, so they could make fun of me. But, little did they know, God had other plans. I would sit at the back of the tent, and the Holy Spirit would hit me, and, somehow, I would end up at the front of the tent dazed and wondering how in heaven's name I got upfront. The Holy Spirit must have really taken control of my body because I would hear everyone laughing, clapping, and praising God after the Spirit turned me loose.

Back then, I knew nothing about being a prophetess, seer, or an assignment. I just knew that the Spirit of the Lord would touch me, and the Holy Ghost would take control. My mother was so intrigued. On the night she came out to the revival, Bishop Polk prophesized on her. This was not expected of her. Unbeknownst to others, my mother was not in plain sight. No one could see that she was there. However, you cannot hide from God, and He knew she was there. God knows where we are always.

As my mother and my cousin hid behind a tall oak tree outside the tent, Bishop Polk, through the Holy Spirit, sensed their presence. Bishop Polk called out and said, "There is a lady standing outside this tent behind a tree; please come in. I have a word for you."

My mother was afraid and would not come inside. Bishop Polk called out again, "Ma'am, please come in. I have something to tell you."

When my mother stepped inside, Bishop Polk was in dismay. She immediately covered her mouth. She knew my mother from high school. She exclaimed, "Oh Laura! Please come forth. Baby, I have some bad news. Someone you love and that is close to you is about to lose their life."

My mother stood in awe. She was not ready to hear, nor did she understand such a prophecy. Her expression told it all. As my mother lowered her head, Bishop Polk told her, "I want you to stretch your hands up high and repeat after me, 'Thank you, Jesus.'"

Momma stretched her hands up high, but as the words began to flow from her mouth, she could only say, "Thanks, Jesus." Tears were flowing down her cheeks, and her voice started to tremble.

Bishop Polk told her to say it again, but faster and louder.

Momma started saying it as fast as she could, "Thank you, Jesus. Thank you, Jesus." But when she got ready to say it a third time, she said, "Thank you, Jesussssssssssss." She received the power of the Holy Spirit that night. Momma's life was changed forever. The Spirit of God touched her, and she became a new person.

The next day, momma and I were sitting in the living room on her brown sofa. We lived in a place called Navy Point. The rain was pouring hard, but something in a tall oak tree in our yard caught my eye. I began crying at what I had seen. Momma asked me, "What's wrong?"

I said, "I just saw this lady with pink hair rollers in her hair." I described the way her hair was rolled up. Then I told her, "The lady was dark, and her eyes were closed and sunk deep into her head."

My mother looked at me and said, "You just described my mother."

I had never met my grandmother. She had passed before I was born. Momma never spoke of her. The only times momma mentioned grandmother was when she told us that she passed when she was seventeen and, if we were acting up, she would tell us that if her mother were alive, we would be different children. In other words, her mother was stringent, and she would fix our sassy, bad behavior real fast with a belt or a switch (two or three limbs from a bush outside). Oh, how

I wish I could hear her utter those words today! Her father, on the other hand, had passed prior to her mother. She never told us how and we never asked. All I knew was his name: Anthony Robinson.

Though my mother is not alive today, at times, I can still hear her voice whispering in my ears and showing up in my dreams. In church, we often sing songs like, "If I could hear my mother pray again, if I could hear her gentle voice again. How happy I would be, would mean so much to me, if I could hear my mother pray again." And, though I would love to hear my mother pray again, I am glad she is an angel that God has watching over me daily. I can feel her protecting me when things seem to go wrong or when I am sad. I say to you, treasure your mother and father while they are still alive because you do not want to be like me, reminiscing about the good times and wishing they were still here. Honor them while they are still alive!

CHAPTER 11: DWELLING
IN MY DREAMS

For God speaketh once, yea twice, yet man perceiveth it not. In a dream, in a vision of the night, when deep sleep falleth upon men, in slumberings upon the bed; Then he openeth the ears of men, and sealeth their instruction, That he may withdraw man from his purpose, and hide pride from man.

Job 33:14-17

Sometimes, the Holy Spirit will visit you while you are asleep, casting upon you dreams that you and He will only know. Most of the time, these dreams are pleasant, but they can be downright scary. Throughout my years, I have documented these dreams in journals and my cell phone as they were provided to me by the Holy Spirit. Be as it may, some dreams tend to slip away shortly after I awaken and will not be revealed until later that day, night, or in life when I have no proof that they ever occurred.

We must take heed to what the Holy Spirit is trying to show us in our dreams. We should be cautious about what He is trying to tell us. For instance, after Mary had given birth to Jesus, an angel of the Lord appeared to Joseph in a dream and said, "Arise, and take the young child and his mother, and flee into Egypt, and be thou there until bring thee word: for Herod will seek he young child to destroy him" (Matthew 2:13). The Holy Spirit was giving Joseph a warning that danger was on the way and that He needed to protect the baby Jesus.

Many times, I have dreamed dreams that have come true. One of my most recent dreams that I would like to share was about my husband, Terry. This dream happened on April 28, 2019, at 6:18 a.m. In the dream, Terry was standing in our front yard and saw what was perceived to him to be a long black rope over by a tree. When he walked towards it, he said, "I believe it's a snake." But before he could turn around, the snake came towards him so fast and bit him on the leg. Terry fell to the ground nearly unconscious.

However, on May 3, 2019, I got extremely sick at work and had to go to the ER. I was hospitalized and sent home on May 5, 2019. Terry and I stopped to pick up my medicine, then went home. For some reason, I decided to go to the back of our house and check on the lawnmowers. I noticed the blue tarp covering the lawnmowers had blown off. Trying to recover the lawnmowers with the tarp, I noticed an area on the right that was sunken in by a puddle of water. As I lifted the tarp to remove the water, I stood in awe for a few moments breathing hard and with fear. There were several grey snakes under the tarp! They were tangled together, nesting. I backed away slowly and ran to the front yard to get Terry. By the time we returned, the snakes had scattered. What I saw in the dream was God warning me instead. Satan meant to cause harm to me that day, but God blocked it.

I think of the many scenarios that could have happened if the snakes had launched out at me or attacked me. I also think about how my husband could have reached for the tarp, and the snakes could've attacked him like in my dream. The Bible says in Psalm 125:3, "For the rod of the wicked shall not rest upon the lot of the righteous; lest the righteous put forth their hands unto iniquity." That day, my hands removed the tarp, but the Lord turned what was meant for evil into something good. God made the devil's rods, the snakes, stay still as I beheld them with my eyes and allowed me to escape

Donna Hodges

without harm.

God had His protective angels around me. Though I dreamed about my husband Terry being bitten by a long black snake, several gray snakes were waiting for me seven days later with evil intent outside our back door. I know God has angels around me, and that day was a prime example of God protecting me and showing me His agape love.

The Bible clearly says in Acts 2:17 (ESV), "And in the last days it shall be, God declares that I will pour out my Sprit on all flesh, and your sons and your daughters shall prophesy, and your young men shall see visions, and your old men shall dream dreams."

Though this was one of many scenarios the Holy Spirit prepared me for through a dream, there are other dreams that have not come true yet, and I am not prepared to face them in the future. We must be cognizant of what the Holy Spirit is revealing to us in our dreams. Many of you may have dreamed about something and never gave a thought to it. I believe the purpose of this chapter is to make you aware of what you are dreaming and to document them in a journal. God is trying to prepare us all for what is to come. God is getting ready to do some things in our lives and on earth that only you will see in your dreams, and you will need to have proof in the future. God wants us to document our visions, dreams, and what we see in the sky. The sky is telling a lot of what is becoming of this world. You have to be obedient and listen to what God is saying.

Donna Hodges

CHAPTER 12: CAUGHT UP ON LOOKS

Hebrews 12:6-7: "For whom the Lord loveth he chasteneth, and scourgeth every son whom he receiveth. If ye endure chastening, God dealeth with you as with sons; for what son is he whom the father chasteneth not?"

This chapter is not only for me but for those out there that suffer from self-esteem problems and are caught up on their outside appearances. I did not understand it at first because the Holy Spirit wanted me to write this novel on the revelations, dreams, and visions He had revealed to me. However, when He woke me up early on January 12, 2020, and told me to write this, I did not flinch. I was obedient as I have been from the beginning. Some may question the significance of this chapter but, when the Holy Spirit speaks to me and tells me to do something, I obey.

This chapter basically explains how something can

deter us from doing the work of the Lord and break our focus from what He wants us to do. Jeremiah 5:5: says, "I will get me unto the great men, and will speak unto them; for they have known the way of the Lord, and the judgment of their God: but these have altogether broken the yoke, and burst the bonds." We must stay focused on what God wants us to do. Let's take a look at how I got so caught up in my appearance that I completely lost focus on what God was trying to do in my life.

From the time I was a little girl until I became an adult, God blessed me with long reddish-brown curly hair. Longer than what my sisters had and prettier than most of my friends around me. I would flaunt my hair, allowing it to blow in the wind like I was a princess, but never realizing how it hurt those that did not have what God had blessed me with.

Early in life, I discovered that God will chastise those He loves in order for us to stay focused on what He has prepared for us to do. As I got older, this became evident when visiting beauty salons. Back in my hometown of Pensacola, Florida, I frequented the beauty salon of Ms. Carry Bell—an incredible lady who always told me, "Donna, your hair is too beautiful to be putting chemicals and hot combs in it to make it straight. You are going to ruin it one day." But I was young and thought I knew better than her. I never paid attention to what she said and, eventually, I started to perm and dye my own hair. My hair was too curly. I wanted straight silky hair that flew in the wind like paper. First Timothy 5:1-2 says, "Rebuke not an elder, but entreat him as a father; and the younger men as brethren; The elder women as mothers and the younger as sisters, with all purity." In other words, God is saying unto us, "Listen to what elders have to say--they are filled with wisdom and knowledge." We may not understand what they are saying at the time but, when we get older, we will remember their words and how they tried to lead us down the path of righteousness.

In 1988, at the age of twenty-one, I joined the United States Navy. I knew I had to cut my hair and was told by recruiters what length it should be. However, they did not tell me that my hair would drastically change during basic training. They cut my hair to the top of my ears, making me look like a man. I was devastated. As I looked in the mirror, I did not see the person I used to be. What man had used for evil, God turned it around for good. The company commander tried to take away my pride and dignity, but God already had my back. You may go in one way, but you surely will come out another. Pride sometimes gets in our way, and we forget who we are and whose we are. I had to realize that life was not about beauty and hair, but is about seeking the Word of God and living according to His commandments. Proverbs 11:2 says, "When pride cometh, then cometh shame: but with the lowly is wisdom."

I dwelled so much on my hair and my looks that I completely forgot that God is a jealous God, and I was idolizing myself over Him. I used to think that it was the only thing I had going for me. God is what I had going for me, not my hair or my looks. You cannot dwell on how you look or how man will see you. You have to put God first in everything you say and do.

In December 2019, God showed me through the prophecy of Deaconess Jackson that I was not to be bothered by what I saw in the mirror but to focus on what God had in store for me. After her prophesy, I started to see a change in my appearance. In late January 2020, I started noticing that my hair was falling out and my face was developing bumps. This was something I tried hard to deal with because I remembered what she had told me. But Satan interrupted my spirit and tried to convince me that God was allowing me to go through this change and that I should defy Him. My face and hair were changing, and it brought me to my lowest. I felt depressed, upset that God was allowing it to happen to me, and I felt like something was wrong. I sought out doctors, and they could not find anything wrong.

Miraculously, on March 24, 2020, the Holy Spirit said, "Look in the mirror!" When I looked in the mirror, I really did not like what I saw. I saw a woman giving up on God and not remembering the prophesy told to me.

The Holy Spirit chastised me. He told me, "The woman with the long hair was someone from your past. I will bring you to a new level in Christ. I am preparing you not to idolize man and what man is made of. Those things will go away, but the Word of God will never end."

Donna Hodges

CHAPTER 13: DAY OF THE BLACK BIRDS

Psalm 91:3: "Surely, he shall deliver thee from the snare of the fowler and from the noisome pestilence."

Commonly known to man, black birds are associated with death and feed on carrion or dead flesh. They hover over maimed animals awaiting their deaths because black birds will not kill the animal themselves. When black birds grace a person's yard, it symbolizes life in heaven. The color black is potentially pure, but not when it comes to vultures, eagles, ravens, red and black kite, the owl, hawk, cormorant, and many others in that family. These birds are unclean and not to be feast upon.

Proverbs 30:17: "The eye that mocketh at his father, and despiseth to obey his mother, the ravens of the valley shall pick it out, and the young eagles shall eat it."

On Monday, March 30, 2020, I was driving to work around 7:27 a.m. The roads were different. Usually, the traffic is at a complete stand still on Route 32 East, and you have to drive like a turtle. Urging myself to stay calm, I usually prayed about the well-being of others that drove foolishly in front and around me. After witnessing too many accidents because people were driving so fast that they ended up in a ditch or crashed, I tended to put on songs of praise to keep myself encouraged and inspired. A few times, I would find myself caught up in the Spirit, and the Holy Spirit takes control. It tends to calm my nerves until I arrive at work.

But on the morning of March 30, 2020, there was an unusual quietness on the road. No rush to get anywhere. Drivers were careful and pleasant for a change. The scare of the coronavirus had the entire world frightened and slowed in their tracks. This was God's time. A time He had already set aside for His saints to gather with their family and fellowship amongst themselves. Employers quickly began to tighten the workloads of their employees. Different shifts were assigned so that no one would spread the virus any further than it had gotten.

The closer I got to my exit on the National Business

Parkway, terror grew in my spirit. I was immediately greeted by a flock of large vultures launching from a ditch. Others hovered over my car and perched themselves on street poles. Fear invaded my mind. In the past, when I saw black birds, it was a sign someone in my family was gravely ill, on the verge of dying, or had sadly passed away. I had to calm my spirit. I suddenly screamed and caused my skin to crawl as the last vulture nearly hit my windshield, trying to catch up with the others. Then, a sigh of relief.

I exhaled and started to pray as I swiftly pulled into a handicap parking space adjacent to my building. I thanked God for delivering me from the pestilent creatures of darkness. I began to confess Psalm 91:4-6,

> He shall cover thee with His feathers and under His wings shalt thou trust: his truth shall be thy shield and buckler. Thou shalt not be afraid for the terror by night; nor for the arrow that flieth by day. Nor for the pestilence that walketh in darkness; nor for the destruction that wasteth at noonday.

I believe that as I grew stronger in faith and began standing on the Word of God, Satan tried everything in his might to bring me down. But I trust and believe that God has angels all around me, protecting me from the evil of this world. God has a plan for my life, and Satan is trying to do everything to deter my thoughts and keep my mind distracted from what is going on around me instead of what God has planned for me.

After thanking God for keeping me safe, I went to work just to receive a call from my former office. Someone had called out, and they needed me to come over and cover until they found a replacement. However, I knew that they would not find one because I was the only Office Manager on that shift and most of the others had self-reported because of Covid. Besides, I had worked this site at the beginning of my career and asked to be removed so that I could go and help a division that was struggling to find an efficient office manager. So, when the other site asked for my assistance, I was ready to help in every way possible and got back in my car.

As I started to drive towards the other office, my eyes fell upon a ravine. Hundreds of huge black vultures were aligned along the gates, the ground, a parking garage, and the ravine were covered with them. One flew towards my car, and I sped up. They were all facing the building at the National Parkway.

I arrived at the parking lot and thanked God for allowing me to make it through this passage of demons. My curiosity got the best of me. What were they trying to tell me? I had never in my life seen so many vultures scattered in one place. Most of the time, these huge pestilent creatures were flying overhead, scouting out dead animals.

Then a thought came to me: What if what the Holy Spirit had told me about "death was upon us" was true? I thought about the nearly ten deaths so far from the coronavirus and how the only thing that could change this outcome was *prayer.* Second Chronicles 7:14 says, "If my people which are called by my name, shall humble themselves and pray, seek my face, and turn from their wicked ways, then will I hear from Heaven and will forgive their sin, and will heal their land." He also said in Psalm 91:7, "A thousand shall fall at thy side, and ten thousand at thy right hand; but it shall not come nigh thee." Millions are being destroyed by the powers of darkness, but those who believe and put their trust in God shall be spared.

Man will never understand that this virus was not created by man or another country because of their selfish denial behavior. Man blames everything on another man but will never acknowledge that God said in His Word, "For God is jealous and the Lord revengeth; the Lord revengeth and is furious and He will take vengeance on His adversaries." Nahum 1: 5-7 says,

> The mountains quake at Him, and the hills melt, and the earth is burned at His presence. Yea, the world, and all that dwell therein. Who can stand before His indignation? And who can abide in the fierceness of His anger? His fury is poured out like fire, and the rocks are thrown down by Him. The Lord is good, a strong hold in the day of trouble, and He knoweth them that trust in Him.

> God is the one that can and will shut down the entire world at one time with a virus and cause the world to go into fear of dying. Man cannot do that alone. Only God can wake up the land, and he that believes otherwise is foolish and will die in their own sins.

In 2007, the Lord God came to me in a dream and said, "Get up!" I did not know why I was getting up, but I was prepared to do what God wanted me to do. The Holy Spirit directed me to get paper and a pen and told me to write this poem in the first person. Why in the first person, you might ask? Because the Lord God had a message for the world, and He wanted me to present it in the way He delivered it to me.

The Spirit that Dwells in Me

When God speaks, we are to listen to what He has to say. This poem not only speaks to what God is saying; death is upon us as His wrath.

God's Wrath

Obey my commandments is all that I ask
but yet you tell a lie;
Make them a part of your daily task
or in your sins you will surely die.
I will send storms a raging—
how the fierce lightning will strike;
Tumbling walls disengaging—
My roar you will not like.
I will make the calm sea rage—
cause a cruise ship to sink;
Your sins must be disengaged
or I will come before you blink.
All the trees will disappear
like the echoes of a clear blue sky;
My wrath will shake the ground that's near
before you can multiply.
Seek and I will destroy
all that you hope to be;
the fires will burn the earth before
I will set you free.
Nation will rise against nation

Donna Hodges

The leaders they will fall;

Causing too much proclamation

trying to protect us all.

All I ask is that you abide

in my word so dear to Me;

My rage of thunder I will hide

if you fall on bended knee.

Donna Brown Hodges

Copyright ©2007

Vultures Attack

On Tuesday, 31 March 2020, 12:15 p.m., I was asked
to assist my former department who was in need of help due
to the Covid-related outages of personnel. My former chief's
calendar made for a rough day. Needless to say, I still had to
work on my current chief's calendar as well. Though the day
was hectic, I still was able to get everything accomplished that
I set out to do. By the time I had finished with everything, my
relief showed up with bags in her hand. I quickly gave her a
brief pass down and went back to my office.

On the way out the door, I ran into a young lady by the
name of Danielle. We started chatting about the coronavirus
as I walked her to her car. Almost immediately, we got on one

accord. It reminded me of Acts 2:1: "And when the day of Pentecost was fully come, they were all with one accord in one place." I began telling her that all of this was taking place because it was biblical, and only God could make it happen. She felt the same way. As we said our goodbyes, we both reached out and shook each other's hands. The governor had said for no one to have any social contact. He mandated for everyone to stay at least six feet away from other people. But when you are believers in God and His Word, you have no fear of man. For we know that God will protect us in any and every situation we encounter if we believe.

I got in my car and began to pray for her and our nation. My cousin Joy Brown taught me back in 1990 to pray every time I got in my car to ask God for protection going and coming without incidence. That way, if something happened to me, God would protect me. As I left the parking lot heading to my original place of business, I remembered the huge vultures from the day before and wondered if they still were in the ravine. Well, my wondering and curiosity did not last long. As soon as I reached the ravine, I turned on my camera in hopes of taking a picture of them to show my husband. Two big vultures were on the lamp pole, distracting my attention as I was trying to take the picture while another one flew right at my car. I scrambled fast, trying to flee from them. The ravine was covered. I believe it was their mating ground and, somehow, I kept disturbing it.

We must be careful when looking for danger because sometimes, the things we look for can come back and haunt us. To date, April 01, 2020, 3:15 p.m., the death toll globally is 45,400 and the amount of people testing positive has reached an astonishing number of 911,400+. When first introduced to this virus, we were told that only fifteen people had been affected in the United States, and that number would quickly be down to zero. Since then, the death toll had grown tremendously. No one knows the power of God. We are living in perilous times with the plagues of Exodus and Revelation upon us. It is time for the world to come together, fast and pray, and ask God for forgiveness so He can heal our nation.

CHAPTER 14: PALM SUNDAY, APRIL 5, 2020

Angels in the Sky

Then I saw another angel flying in the midst of heaven, having the everlasting gospel to preach to those who dwell on the earth—to every nation, tribe, tongue, and people—saying with a loud voice, "Fear God and give glory to Him, for the hour of His judgment has come, and worship Him who made heaven and earth, the sea, and springs of water."

Revelation 14:6-7 (NKJV)

Angels have been upon earth since the beginning. Many have witnessed the appearances of angels, but few will believe without proof. How can one perceive an existence that many do not believe in or comprehend? I am one that believes and knows that God will show wonders to those that believe. God showed His wonders to me at the same place He revealed the sword, two dark figures, a crystalized glowing cross, and darkness in the sun—River of Life Worship Center.

Prayer service was commencing, and still, we could not have more than ten individuals gathering inside our church. Not realizing that this Sunday was prayer service on the inside for men only, I walked inside and was quickly reminded. What a blessing it turned out to be! After paying my tithes, offerings, and the sacrificial offering from our three-day fast, I went outside and placed my Bible and purse in my car. Though I wanted to join the women walking and worshipping outside, the Holy Spirit told me that I must stay focused. Of course, I did not know what that meant but, as I continued to walk, I came upon three church vans. I gazed into the sky and saw an angel and other faces. The sun was to my left, and the angel was to my right.

At first, I thought I was seeing things, so I continued to walk toward my car. Then, the Holy Spirit said to me, "Get your cell phone and take a picture." He knew if I told people about seeing an angel in the sky, no one would believe me. I got my phone and took several pictures because I could not believe what I was seeing. When I looked at my cell phone, the picture of the angel was there. I began to worship God in the Spirit. I wanted to get a closer picture, but the Holy Spirit instructed me to put the phone back in my car. I obeyed, and I walked over to the point where I saw the angel. It was still there. I could feel the sun shining down to the left of me, but I did not want to take a chance by looking at it again. I was afraid of going blind.

Other than the angel I had seen, there were two very evil faces on the left that I did not capture. One was of a huge bird, and the other I could not make out. It only had eyes, a nose, and a mouth, but it was extremely evil. I started to pray, asking God to remove the evil from the earth and to cover us with His Blood. The Holy Spirit turned me towards the sun and had me look upon it again. I was afraid, but He calmed my spirits. As I prayed and worshipped in the spirit, some of the ladies came by playing music and singing, but I continued to seek His glory. Sometimes, I wondered what was going through their minds as they witnessed me looking at the sun. Did they know what God was revealing, or did they think I had lost my mind? Either way, it did not matter. God had me on a mission to testify to the world about His glory, and I was not going to disappoint Him.

The Holy Spirit removed my eyes and had me walk around the parking lot again. By the time I made it back to the three vans, the angel and the faces were gone. God was letting me know that He indeed heard my prayer of removing the evil from this world and that He was in control. A thick cloud had covered it. As I began to praise God, my eyes returned to the sun just in time to see a shining cross sparkling and glistening with diamond-like jewels all around it. There were three golden torches that kept appearing on the left side of the sun and a bright yellow light down the middle. A ring of beautiful colors surrounded the outside of the sun, and I stood in awe of God's beauty. Then, the Holy Spirit removed my eyes, and I began to slowly walk on the black asphalt. I felt very faint. I mean—was it truly possible to have two encounters with the sun and live to talk about it?

Why did God choose someone like me? Was I even worthy? I am a woman that had experienced so much pain and hurt throughout my life. I cared for others that could not care for themselves, loved on mankind when others passed them by, gave to the homeless along the highways. And yet, at one time, did some things that were not pleasing to God. But God, with all His glory and love, still chose me to be a disciple of Christ and witness to the world of His miraculous powers!

While walking toward the front of our church, there was writing on the sidewalk that said, "This Too Shall Pass!" Confirmation that, once again, God was in control. There were some ladies from the dance ministry walking in the distance behind me. They were playing music, and a familiar song came on. I had not allowed anything to interrupt me thus far, but when the singer sang, "Way Maker, Miracle Worker, Promise Keeper, Light in the Darkness, My God that is Who You are!" I turned around with the glory of the Lord upon me and began singing, shouting, and dancing all over the parking lot until I almost fell over.

My hands reached towards to sky, where the sun was brightly shining over the steeple of our church. Several black birds flew towards the sun, and I was afraid. I tried counting them, but my mind would not allow me. The Holy Spirit said, "Stay focused!" which is something my best friend, Prophetess Pamela Hunter, is always telling me. I could see one of the ladies walk into the church as I stood in the middle of the road praising God and worshipping Him. As others drew near, I continued my praise.

Then the Holy Spirit said, "Go to your car!" It was right behind me. But as I turned around, I could see the birds flying away from the sun, and I counted eight of them. I did not say anything to anyone. I just got in. A text message chimed at 9:55 a.m. from my youngest brother's girlfriend, "Good morning. All is well. Girl, we got to keep your brother in prayer in that prison with this virus going on. I pray he will be alright. I know he will be glad when he gets released. Okay! You all stay safe and have a blessed day."

Again, the Holy Spirit removed me from my car, and I leaned against the front hood. I began to pray for my brother and everyone that was affected by the virus. At that point, the sun was bright yellow, and beautiful colors were around it. I smiled, knowing that, among all these people, God allowed me to see His holiness in the sun again. Who would not serve a God like this?

The Holy Spirit removed my eyes and told me to look at the marquee in the field. At first, it had a blur, but God soon corrected my eyes so that I could see it clearly. I was afraid of losing my sight, but the Holy Spirit said to me, "Your sight will not be lost, my child. I have you covered."

Donna Hodges

CHAPTER 15: LET GO AND LET GOD

Psalm 55:22: "Cast thy burden upon the Lord and He shall sustain thee: he shall never suffer the righteous to be moved."

There is a beckoning in my soul from the Holy Spirit saying, "I am bigger than that problem you have." Just when you thought everything was going well, the devil comes along and causes chaos. Before the pandemic, perhaps you had a great job, great family, and plans to renew your vows in an exotic getaway in the Caribbean. But, out of nowhere, life happened: restrictions were placed on vacation spots, hotels, visitations, etc. You went and bought all types of things for your trip. You lost your job, and finances became an issue because you could not replenish what you paid in preparation for your trip. Depression set in, and now you are at wits' end trying to find a solution.

In this time of struggle, you must realize that you cannot carry this burden by yourself. You must give it to God and let Him handle it for you. God knows our every burden. He wants us to submit ourselves unto Him. He can handle anything, even those things we consider to be small. Just ask in our Father's name, and He will give us the desires of our hearts. God said, "He is the beginning and end of all our cares." Think about it. How many times have you made that same recipe and, the one time you made it for someone else, it just did not come out right? You used all the same ingredients, mixed it the same amount of time, but it came out runny or lumpy. You could not figure out what you did wrong. It is the same with God. You have prayed repeatedly for things to change in your life, and just when you were about to give up, God stepped in and fixed it for you.

When we let go of our problems and let God handle them, things change. There is nothing too big for God. You just have to have faith, trust, and believe that God will handle it for you.

In Proverbs 27:1, the Spirit of the Lord saith unto us, "Boast not thyself of tomorrow, for thou knowest not what a day may bring forth." He furthered this sentiment in

Matthew 6:33, "But seek ye first the kingdom of God, and his righteousness and all these things shall be added unto you."

CHAPTER 16: DELIVERANCE BY THE SPIRIT

Jeremiah 17:14: "Heal me, O Lord, and I shall be healed; save me and I shall be saved: for thou art my praise."

Matthew 4:23: "For it was Jesus who went through Galilee, teaching in their synagogues, preaching the gospel of the kingdom, and healing all manner of sickness and all manner of disease among the people."

These things are evidence that Jesus, through His Father God, is a healer of sickness and can cure any disease. He is a divine strengthener of faith to those that believe. For many years, I had suffered chronic migraines and back, leg, and many other pains within my body. I prayed to God for healing and believing that one day it would all go away. Many days and nights, I would beg and plead for deliverance because the pain was so severe. I would take prescription medicines and over-the-counter medicines to find relief but to no avail.

Then, the Holy Spirit guided me to write this book that could be a witness for many generations to come. So, on April 17, 2020, I had a talk with the Lord, pouring out my soul to Him and letting Him know that I was tired—tired of the migraines, tired of the back pain, leg pain, losing my hair, getting bumps on my face—I was just plain tired.

I had been boastful about never having had bumps on my face months before that talk with God. Unfortunately, I must've spoken it into existence because, miraculously, in February 2020, my face started to develop bumps from out of nowhere. I freaked out.

Satan heard me speak those boastful words and proclaim something that I did not have: bumps. What better way to hinder me from doing the will of God and keep me from completing the assignment that God placed me on! When we speak these things into existence and Satan hears them, he will cast them upon us and leave us feeling helpless.

After complaining, losing sight, and focus on what God had in store for me, the Holy Spirit whispered in my ear, "My child, this too shall come to pass." It was amazing to hear those words from the Holy Spirit.

Then, the Holy Spirit led me into prayer: "Our Father, who art in heaven, I thank you first and foremost for your Son Jesus, for allowing Him to sacrifice His life for someone I deem to be unworthy of Him. I want to thank you for waking me up this morning closed in my right frame of mind. Dear God, thank you for being God all by yourself. Now, Lord, I come to you once again asking and seeking your help. Lord, I have been praying for deliverance from these migraines for years." At this point, the Holy Spirit had me place my hand on my head and my face as I continued to pray. "Father God, I thank you for what you are about to do. Lord, I have been taking many over-the-counter medicines and prescription medicines for the past thirty years, and I'm tired. I need your deliverance right now in the mighty name of Jesus."

Again, the power of the Holy Spirit took control and began to work in my body. I could feel my insides being healed and delivered as I touched my head, my face, and my body. Not only was God healing my body, but He was also renewing my soul so that I could stay focused on what He wanted me to do. The power of God delivered me, and I claimed victory over my sickness.

For the first time in years, I went without taking BC

Powders, something I had been using for years to relieve the migraines headaches. You see, when we take time to talk to God and tell Him what we want, He will give us our heart's desire and what we need as well.

I decree and declare: By the power of the Almighty, I have been set free, been delivered, and made complete. I am truly walking in victory.

CHAPTER 17: MESSAGES OF HOPE

A Dying Soul: July 12, 2019, Warrington, FL

Acts 24:15 (ESV): "Having a hope in God, which these men themselves accept, that there will be a resurrection of both the just and the unjust."

I wanted to tell her that everything would be alright, that the nightmares shadowing her dreams would soon be over, and how using different drugs and medications to try to relax her mind could poison her soul. But what I did tell her was that God loved her and would be there for her if she submitted herself fully and completely to the will of God.

As I was delivering a message of God's love to one lost soul, another hungry soul knocked on the door. The message of deliverance was not finished, but when the knock came, and she loudly asked, "Who is it?" Opportunity replied, "Me!"

At first, the voice sounded familiar, like a man I used

to know that terrorized the neighborhood, beating, killing, and fracturing the lives of innocent people. Fear ran through my mind as the door opened. But it was not him. It was a tall, dark-skinned friendly guy looking for a hit to hold him over.

"This is my friend, Donna," the woman said as I held her hands tightly, trying to deliver her from the whispers inundating her mind with thoughts of suicide and depression.

"What you want?" she asked.

"I was wondering if I could buy a blunt?" He peeped his head through her white door.

Now the power of the Holy Spirit took over me, and my hands released my friend's, and my mouth spoke boldly with power. "Come here," I told the young man with no shirt on his skinny body, sagging pants, and a white T-Shirt wrapped around his neck.

"You see, what I thought the Holy Spirit was bringing me from Maryland to do at my friend's house was, in fact, for the company that came to her house. 'Look at God!'"

As he walked nervously toward me, my heart started to pound heavily as I thought of what I might say. Who was I but a messenger of Christ trying to save a dying world? I reached for his hand as my friend told him, "This is my good friend, Donna, from childhood." Then she turned to me and said, "Donna, he is worse off than me."

It was at that point the Holy Spirit spoke words into my mouth with a message of hope and encouragement. As I looked into the eyes of a hungry, torn young man, I could see the hurt, pain, and suffering he had endured his entire life. The Holy Spirit allowed me to see through to his heart. Through me, the Holy Spirit asked, "Do you know God loves you?"

Shattered by those six words, this young man began to wipe his right eye. Again, I repeated, "Do you know God loves you?" I felt in my spirit that I was not just ministering to this young man, but somebody reading this today needed to hear those words. "He wants you to submit yourself to Him and be delivered from the spirits of drugs, depression, and loneliness." He wiped his eyes even more. "The Lord said, 'Clean yourself up and present yourself as a changed man so that He can use you and give you the desires of your heart.'" With every word said and every revelation the Holy Spirit poured into his soul, he wiped his eyes. "Now, ask yourself this, 'Do I want a blunt because others are using them? Or, do I need a blunt because you need it to take away your pain and help remove you from the situation you are in with others tempting you to be like them?'"

Massive tears came from his eyes. I could see him being reached and the Holy Spirit pouring love into the man's dying soul.

"God loves you," the Holy Spirit boldly expressed to him once again as I laid my hands on his back, watching his body weaken and almost fall limp to my touch. I held him while speaking the words that the Holy Spirit planted in my mind for him.

> And ye have respect to him that weareth the gay clothing, and say unto him, Sit thou here in a good place; and say to the poor, Stand thou there, or sit here under my footstool; Are ye not then partial in yourselves, and are become judges of evil thoughts?
>
> James 2:3-4

The white door at the front of the house slowly opened again, and standing there was another lost soul looking for the delivered man. He was the reason the man was buying the blunt. He was desire and destruction. His purpose was to make this guy's life complicated. He was a familiar face. He called out to him.

I whispered in his ear, "Remember what I told you.

You are strong. You do not need help through drugs. You need God's help. God loves you."

He walked away into the kitchen, looking back at me from time to time. I could tell that I had reached him. I heard the familiar voice say, "Frank, what was she telling you?"

He responded, "I don't want or need any drugs. I'll see you later." Then he took the white T-Shirt from around his neck and pulled it over his head.

I called out to him, "Remember what we talked about," I reminded him as he began walking towards the door.

"Yes, ma'am," he smiled as he headed out the door.

The next day, my friend informed me that Frank had cut his hair and put on a clean shirt. This young man was homeless, going from house to house trying to find a place to lay his head at night. God wanted him to know that He heard his cries and saw his struggles. God is a way maker. He can fix anything in our lives if we open up and let Him in. This young man had received God's Word and was working his way towards greatness.

The Lord wants us to help those that are struggling and judging them by the way they live their lives. Many are blessed to have a good life, but there are others who choose to live life dangerously. They have not received the fulfillment of Christ and have not heard about His goodness.

How many times have we, as a society, given up on life or Christ and tried to hide our sorrows by using drugs, drinking alcohol, smoking cigarettes and weed, or taking pills to relieve our pain? Has anyone ever told you that "God loves you" or told you about Christ? It is never too late to come to Christ. We must be believers and doers of His Word.

Update on Frank-February 13, 2021

It had been nearly two years since I testified to Frank. Today, at 5:22 p.m., I was talking to my sister, and I was telling her about Frank and how things happened that faithful day. She cut me off and said, "Girl! Frank came to me and said, 'When your sister laid her hands on my back, I thought I was going to pass out.'" My sister informed me that she speaks to Frank all the time, and he talks a lot about how I changed his life. He said, "She made my legs buckle." My sister also told me that Frank is no longer homeless and doesn't wear raggedy clothing or beg for handouts anymore. He keeps himself clean because, after receiving Christ that day, he got a good job and found somewhere to stay.

I started telling her how we were interrupted by a guy that came looking for Frank. Miraculously, at that very moment, a knock was at my sister's door, and, low and behold, Frank and the guy were standing there in her doorway. Do you see how God works? You can be talking about someone or something, and God will present it in the present. She told him that she was talking to me. I immediately asked to talk to him.

"Hello," he said.

"Oh, my God! Frank, you sound so good."

"Yes, ma'am," he responded. "Thank you so much for what you did that day. I am doing good, just like you said. I have a job and everything."

"I heard. I told you, God loves you, and He has great things in store for you if you give your life to Him. You just have to believe in yourself. I am so proud of you, Frank."

"Yes, ma'am."

Then, the other young man said, "Hi, auntie. How are you?"

"I am doing well, sweetheart. How about you?"

"I have changed my life also. I saw how things were going for Frank, and I decided to do that same thing. I am getting my life together."

"That's good, baby! I am so proud of you both. I love you so much."

"Yes, ma'am. I love you too, auntie," he replied and handed the phone back to my sister.

This is how I know the Holy Spirit dwells in me. God will place you in the right place at the right time and work miracles in the lives of the oppressed. These two young men were lost, but God interceded and changed their lives for the better. We must encourage others to seek the kingdom of God and let them know that God loves them. If we do not and are too proud to go into the poorest of neighborhoods and pour out God's love to them, then we are no better as Christians than the sinner.

Losing All Hope, July 13, 2019, Warrington, FL

Proverbs 10:28 (ESV): "The hope of the righteous brings joy, but the expectation of the wicked will perish."

We do not understand why people choose to live their lives dependent upon others or drugs for survival. Some people do not know any other way to live without reaching out to others for a helping hand. I met this young lady with long brown hair while sitting in the living room of a friend. She had two children, and the entire house was filled with children from other people. I was totally amazed. The young lady was dressed as though the summer's heat had gotten the best of her. The desire to go outside had not crossed anyone's mind on this beautiful Saturday afternoon. The torn sofa and loveseat were given to the young lady as a gift for helping with her children. Defeat embraced the young lady's face after hearing me state, "Who cut up the arms of the sofa and the pillows that I sat on?"

A reply kept coming from the kitchen, "Pattie."

"Who's Pattie?" Someone should have to pay for the damage that happened to my friend's furniture. But, little did I know, Pattie was the mother of all the children running around. She needed a place to stay, and my friend told her that she, her boyfriend, and the kids could stay with her.

I was taken aback. I had already passed judgment and crucified the lady while she stood in the midst, listening to what I was saying. I thought, *What kind of Christian was I to minister to others about Christ but scorn someone less fortunate than myself for something I had no business being involved in?*

The child that had torn the furniture into pieces was a

three-year-old toddler that belonged to the woman whose house I was visiting. Unbeknownst to me, the apartment belonged to the woman standing in the kitchen watching me put her down. My friend had given up the apartment and allowed the young lady to live there with her family. My friend moved in with her boyfriend until the family could find a place of their own to live.

As we spoke more about our childhood days and how times had changed for the both of us, I spoke about the young man I had prophesized and prayed for the day prior. I told her that he began to tear up when I asked him, "Do you know that God loves you?" Just mentioning the words brought tears to my friend's eyes. I knew the Holy Spirit was about to use me to witness and pray for her at that point. Staring into her eyes, I led her to the backroom of the apartment and began to witness to her about God's love.

The room was filled with clothes and other items scattered all over the floor. It was a total disaster. I shook my head, thinking, *Who lives like this?* As my friend began to make excuses about how the woman did not clean up behind herself and the kids, the woman walked into the room, retrieved some items, and left. She could see I was deep into a spiritual conversation with my friend, and we needed to be alone.

The power of the Holy Spirit was great and mighty. It fell upon us as her eyes filled with tears. Myra wanted and needed deliverance. She needed healing for her mind, soul, and body. She was thirsty for Christ.

What the Holy Spirit did next was no stranger to me. He looked deep into her soul and pulled out the innocence that had been taken from her as a child. He wanted her full attention. He told her that for too long, she had relied on others for help and became dependent upon others to help make it through life. He told her that He knew she had lived a rough life, but God was going to deliver her that day—that moment, if only she submitted herself completely and fully to Him. We went to the floor, kneeling by the spirit that embraced both of us. Through the Holy Spirit, I spoke by the power of the Almighty with tongues, touching and healing her body. As soon as I asked if she accepted what God had done for her and received a confirmation, Myra was delivered from her sins and healed from her sicknesses. She embraced God as her Savior.

No Peace at Home-July 13, 2019, Pensacola, FL

Philippians 4:7: "And the peace of God, which

surpasseth all understanding, shall keep your hearts and your minds through Christ Jesus."

Life took away her hope. As a child, she had to listen to her name being called in vain, her mother slapping her face, and the men she poured her heart into abusing her body. Being a mother and grandmother were her greatest accomplishments. She sought love where love was not. Being a product of abuse, it was no different when the men she loved abused her. It was normal, but it was not love.

I am sure they told her they loved her, but their actions showed something different. One man after another, she provided her love, but love was not there for her. After the death of her second husband, she longed for a love she once had in high school. A love that would give her hope, stability, and belief in herself to help her forget about her past and remember her future.

However, after marrying her high school sweetheart, the love she sought drifted and faded away. Jealousy swept in, and problems started to arise. Compliments went away, and loneliness embraced her heart. The man that once provided happiness no longer existed. Devastation dwelled in her heart. Sadness poured into her eyes. No matter what she did, it was never enough. He ceased to acknowledge her presence. He did not appreciate what she had to offer.

Although he married her, he was still hurt by old lovers. He did not want his heart broken again. There's an old man's mentality that blanket many men. He had that. "A woman's place is in the home, not the streets or at work. A man needs relaxation after a hard day's work, and the woman needs to take care of the house. Why waste the rest of your day doing things around the house when a beer and a lawn chair work better. Women say they need love, but what they really want is a provider. A man's home is his castle, and women are there for one reason—to keep it clean!" This was the mentality of men in the 1960s and 1970s. But here she was living in 2019, and he was stuck in the past. Unfortunately, there are still men who still think this way.

When we allow obstacles to construct the love we have in our hearts, life is met with challenges. James 1: 2-4: "My brethren, count it all joy when ye fall into divers' temptations; Knowing this, that the trying of your faith worketh patience. But let patience have her perfect work, that ye may be perfect and entire, wanting nothing." James 1:8: "A double minded man is unstable in all his ways."

After ministering to this young lady about how it takes time to remove the pain from a man's heart, I gave her some pointers that had helped me along the way when I, too, was having issues with my husband. When the Holy Spirit showed me how to resolve the issues, I passed them along to my friend who was seeking help.

Now the couple is on social media and how God has interceded in their life. The challenges they were having turned to a happy ending.

CHAPTER 18: TRANSFORMING SPIRITS

Ecclesiastes 1:14: "I have seen all works done under the sun; and, behold all is vanity and vexation of spirit." The preacher or King Solomon is suggesting that we, as Christians, try and gain all that we can while we are living, but we forget about what happens when we are gone. We cannot take it with us. Though some try to have their vanity buried in their graves with them, it will all vanish when we die. If there is much to gain, it will be passed around from generation to generation. After King Solomon built houses, planted trees, built a pool, and had all the silver and gold he could gain, he realized that he had nothing. All was vanity and vexation. It gave him false pride, and it irritated him.

We, as Christians, must transform our spirit into one that only God controls. Transformation happens when a complete shifting or restructuring of the mind, body, soul, and spirit connects with one another and gets on one accord. If one is missing, the others cannot fully function. Saints have been practicing this notion for generations, and the Holy Spirit uses each component differently to form an inimitability in the realm of God. During this process, the saints are tested to see if they are truly men and women of God.

With all the insights the Holy Spirit has shown me, we must transform ourselves into what God wants us to be. In order for this to happen, these four transformations must take place in the realm of God:

Transformation of the Body:

Mark 1:3: "The voice of one crying in the wilderness, prepare ye the way of the Lord, make his paths straight." This allows you to shape your body into readiness for Christ so that He can use you as His warrior. Many people have gotten so comfortable with the way their bodies are that you would hear them say, "If God wanted me to be a certain way, He would have made me that way." In reality, God created us to be who He wants us to be and not what we want to be. We were created in God's image without a spot.

Ask yourself: Does transforming your body into something you want it to be aligned with what God wants it to be? The process of transforming means that you have to make changes in your body and your life. It can be a diet, a change in your health, a spiritual body cleansing, or any type of change to make you feel good about yourself. In May 2019, I joined a fitness boot camp and began transforming my body. I wanted to be ready in case God had a task for me. My mind would be capable of achieving what He wants, and I would be physically, emotionally, and psychologically ready to take it on.

Losing fifteen pounds meant a lot to me, but I was still missing something. I had not transformed my mind to adjust to the changes I had just made. Though my body had started to look and feel good, my mind could not handle the dietary adjustments I had made. I gradually started to wean myself off the diet and, eventually, stopped attending the boot camp program after the initial six weeks were complete. Because of that, I started back gaining the weight that I had lost, and my body was not aligning with what God had for me.

When I noticed how my body began transforming back to the way it used to be, I thought about how we as Christians get saved, sanctified, and filled with the Holy Ghost professing God as our Savior. But after the enjoyment is gone, we allow others to get in our ears, and, eventually, we start looking like the world again. Society will take note of what has become of you and your life and see that you have made a change.

Consequently, your own family and so-called friends will pull away from you. They no longer want to be around you because you not only changed your body, but you also changed the way you think and the way you speak. You have become deeper into the Word of God and, when we start to speak of Him, most people shy away. Believe it or not, most people do not want to hear how you have changed your life. They just want to live and enjoy life for what it is worth.

We have to find ways to communicate with others. By helping them develop a life-changing experience, such as our Christian walk through faith, we can help change their mindset and beliefs in themselves.

Transformation of the Mind

Second Timothy 1:7: "For God hath not given us the spirit of fear; but of power and of love, and of a sound mind."

"Build your mind to think positive and not negative thoughts. As the Lord reveals Himself to you, be not afraid for He is with you through your fears, your pain and suffering, finances, and your illnesses. God has given you power over your mind to deliver others from any iniquity." I can hear the Holy Spirit saying to me. Amen.

Transformation of the Spirit

Ezekiel 11:19: "And I will give them one heart, and I will put a new spirit within you; and I will take the stony heart out of their flesh, and will give them a heart of flesh."

When the Spirit of the Lord comes upon us, it changes who we are and what we believe in. This encounter takes place with the Holy Spirit or an encounter with God. During this process, you will experience joy, salvation, and an intimate talk between you and God through the Holy Spirit. It is something that only a few people have experienced, and many churches do not espound on. It is not common to see worshippers speak in the Spirit in churches outside of Pentecostal, Worship Centers, or what used to be called "The Sanctified Church." To fully embrace and receive the power of the Holy Spirit and be in the presence of the Lord, you will have to be amongst the thousands that truly worship in the Spirit of God. Acts 2:1: "And when the day of Pentecost was fully come; they were all with one accord in one place." Meaning, the Spirit of the Lord was upon them, and all spoke with different tongues.

We often hear someone say the expression, "I'm saved,

sanctified, and filled with the Holy Ghost." In essence, can one truly know that they are saved, sanctified, and filled with the Holy Ghost? The answer to the question is *yes*. Without a shadow of doubt, if you are asked if you are saved, the Bible teaches us to say, "I believe that the Lord saved me with His spirit."

A good friend of mine once told me that she does not believe that people can actually speak in the Spirit. I asked her, "If you have been saved your entire life, how is it that you do not know about worshipping in the Spirit or speaking in the Spirit?"

She said, "That's not the way my church taught us."

This left me baffled as to what was being said in the house of the Lord. If we do not teach others about the Holy Spirit, how will they know about the complete transformation of God?

Transformation of the Soul

Job 27:8: "For what is the hope of the hypocrite, though he hath gained, when God taketh away his soul?"

The Bible teaches us that when the soul is transformed from the body, it ascends into heaven or descends into hell. Without the connection of the body, mind, and spirit, the soul is lost.

CHAPTER 19: THE CROSS OF SALVATION

Matthew 10:37-38: "He that loveth father or mother more than me is not worthy of me and he that loveth son or daughter more than me is not worthy of me. And he that taketh not his cross and followeth after me is not worthy of me."

The voice of God is speaking to His church, for He has seen His people cling to their earthly parents and children more than they praise Him. God wants us to worship Him and Him only.

As the preacher stood in the pulpit looking out at his parishioners, he posed a question. "Will you come? Will you give your life to Christ before it's too late?"

Silence captured a room filled with believers and those that were not. The cross that came to me in a dream with Jesus' face in front of it was being offered to many, but none came.

No one had the nerve to walk up front where many preachers, prophets, and prophetesses had stood offering salvation and redemption for their sins.

The back door to the church opened, and suddenly an unknown man with dirty clothes walked in. He wanted not to beg for something to eat or drink, but he wanted to receive the living water so that he would never thirst again. John 4:10 says, "Jesus answered and said unto her, If thou knewest the gift of God, and who it is that saith to thee, Give me to drink; thou wouldest have asked of him, and he would have given thee living water."

Jesus gave up His life even for a murderer like Barabbas, who killed many. Jesus took his place on the cross of salvation. He died so that we might be saved. He gave His life for us, so we would not have to suffer.

Can you imagine sitting at home and the Holy Spirit telling you to get up and go to a prayer service when you know a virus or plague has hit the entire world? But you, having faith and hearing from God, get in your car as an obedient servant, although you do not know what is about to happen to you. This phenomenon that changed my life will forever play in my head.

Now, imagine coming out of church after prayer service and having the Holy Spirit tell you to get in your car and pull into another parking space? Who does that? Although I could have easily walked over to where He wanted me to be. But, that's not how God works. He puts us in the right place at the right time. He tells us the whens, wheres, whats, and the hows to do in life so that it will be made perfect to Him.

Here is the greatest imagination of all: Believing that God can do anything at any time for anybody. When the Holy Spirit spoke to me and said, "Go into the field and look upon the sky!" I reached the point where God wanted me to be—at His glory—the sun on its brightest day. At the peak of brightness.

God allowed me to gaze into something I believe no man has ever done before without covering their eyes, hurting their eyes, or without sunglasses. Imagine God using you or me to do something so great that when you try to tell others about it, you are consumed by the Spirit of God! But the glory that was inside the sun was the cross, the sword, and the altar. How badly I wanted to fall upon my knees and give God the glory! But He would not allow me to because He knew I would have missed what He wanted me to see. What would have happened if I had not been obedient and listened to the Holy Spirit? You would not know or believe the miraculous powers of God. But I was obedient, and I did listen because I know when the Holy Spirit speaks to me, He has a message for the world, and I must be obedient and adhere to His Word.

What kind of God allows us to see things and come back as a witness to tell the world what we have seen? Let me tell you what kind of God does that! My Lord and Savior Jesus Christ, God of Jehovah, the King of Kings—He allows us to do these things. When we believe and trust in God, there are no limits to what God will reveal to us. Someone must continue God's prophesies and be a witness to those who are lost and do not believe in the powers of the Holy Spirit.

God said in Psalm 37:4, "Delight thyself also in the Lord, and He shall give thee the desires of thine heart." Look toward the cross for redemption, revival of the heart, faith with the courage to believe, and an understanding love. When God showed me all that was inside of the sun to include the darkness that will come to the world, which I believe is greater than the coronavirus, I yielded myself to Him. I need God's glory surrounding me every day of every second, of every minute of every hour. We must position ourselves to believe, receive, and achieve what God has in store for us.

Donna Hodges

CHAPTER 20: CHASTISEMENT
OF THE FAITH

Imagine! Going to church on Resurrection Sunday at sunrise, the parking lot is empty, darkness all around you, and the doors are closed. You sit in your car, anxious, just waiting to see if anyone would come. But then, you remember, there is something called the "coronavirus" and a pandemic. You are told that you cannot worship with more than ten people. What in the world is going on? For the first time in your life, you are told that you cannot go to the house of the Lord and worship Jesus on the day of His resurrection. What kind of ridiculousness is that? Cannot worship in the Lord's house on Resurrection Day? Never heard of such a thing! But it happened. Not just in the United States but throughout the world. Churches completely shut their doors.

Then you hear the voice of the Lord say, "It's not about

you, but it is about Him, His Word, and our faith in Him."

God sent His Son to bear witness to us that He exists. But man, through worldly gain, saw fit to profit on one of the holiest days of the year. Greed set in, and mankind gained so much with their businesses, even building what is depicted as "Mega Churches" to lure people in and cash in on the birth of Christ and His resurrection.

"It's not about you, but the seed you sow and develop through the Word of God," saith the Lord. You know the saddest sight I have ever seen was not the death of my mother or father, but going to church on what is referred to by man as "Easter Sunday" and no one is there but me, five deer at the playground, the Word of God, and songs playing on my radio like "Because He Lives" and "This is Amazing Grace." No one came out to witness the rising of the sun on this day because the coronavirus put a restriction on mankind. Can you believe that? A restriction was placed on mankind, so on Resurrection Sunday, April 12, 2020, only ten people could gather to worship the Lord on His holiest day!

I believe that God wanted to see who would be faithful and still come out and praise His name regardless of what man said. Jesus laid down His life so that we would not be afraid of what we could see but that we would fear God only. As I sat in my car waiting for the sun to rise, I began reading John chapters 19 and 20 (The Crucifixion of Christ and The Resurrection of Christ) in their entirety. Being as anxious as I was to be in the presence of the Lord, I began allowing distractions to interfere with why I had come out to worship and glorify Him.

Within minutes, a police officer slowly drove past me, circling around the church. Fear encamped my mind and interrupted what I had begun to read. I just knew he would stop his car and ask, "Why are you sitting out in the parking lot alone?" But he kept driving by and, eventually, he left. The Holy Spirit motioned me to continue to read but, as I got a little further, I kept turning around looking for the sun so that I could capture it rising with me in the background. Then, I kept turning around to make sure no one would sneak behind me and attack me. *Fear* was overcoming me, and the Scriptures that I was reading were *broken*. I was completely missing the true meaning as to why I was there—To be in the presence of God!

"It's not about you!" I heard the voice say again. "It's about God, Christ, and the Resurrection." What did it profit me to have a picture of the sun rising and me in it if I missed the words that God put in front of me?" God *chastised* me. The guilt that I felt made me feel worthless and ashamed. I had been talking about going to church on Resurrection Sunday all week to whoever would listen at sunrise but, when I got there, seeing the deer, police office, and a few black birds flying on top of our church, I was distracted. As I sat in my car and worshipped in song and praise, rejoicing in the Spirit, I began to pray. I picked the Word up again and started to read. I completely missed the purpose of my being there and my blessing.

Though I was by myself, God was with me. He knew my faithfulness, and I embraced it knowing that God, Jesus, and the Holy Spirit were with me. It was not for others to come out and rejoice with me, especially if they had never done it before. It was my time to give reverence to God—to truly feel and celebrate the resurrection of Jesus Christ. After I knew what God had in store for me, I drove away feeling ashamed. But the Holy Spirit said, "Lift your head up, my child! At least, you came, and you saw!" A smile embraced my face because God knew my heart, and He knew that I came with so much excitement that I allowed fear and distractions to get in my way. Though God did not reveal what I had hoped to see—

another sign in the sky or something dramatic—He showed me that the true meaning of His resurrection resides in the people who believe, trust, worship, and follow Him.

Idolizing Easter Not Christ Resurrection—A Message from God

Man has worshipped on Resurrection Sunday every year for almost a century for all the wrong reasons. They run to hair salons, nail salons, the mall, pull out their best hats, and buy the most outlandish dresses and suits so they would be recognized by others for the way they look. The two most worshipped days of the year are Christmas and Easter, and man capitalizes on them. Retail stores put out the best that they have so that man will buy. Other stores put out Easter baskets, buckets, chocolate candy, ham, and more so the industry can profit.

But, this year, God shut it all down. There was no going to the malls, the retail stores, or even to church. The false prophets or so-called men of God waiting to cash in on the people could not profit. Sure, most preachers preach the Word of God and are honest about their faith. But many forgot what the true meaning of the resurrection is and try to capitalize on their parishioners. God is tired of man's fake beliefs, idolizing the world, worshipping other gods, and not Him. The things that we buy to make ourselves look good are idols, and they are used for the glorification of man. They do not glorify God.

Churches around the world were stunned and left in limbo, not knowing what to do on Resurrection Sunday, April 12, 2020. But some worshippers went against what their governors and the President said, and they conducted service as usual, and this honored God, not man. God loves the faithfulness of His people. They did not allow man to stop them, including myself, from worshipping and bringing forth the Word of God. We had faith in God, knowing that none of the parishioners would get sick from the coronavirus. By worshipping God on His holy day, we gave the message that if God is for us, who can be against us.

Until we give complete utterance and praise to God, He will continue His fiery torment and, eventually, cast us out of His sight. For we are creatures of habit, and we all need to change.

CHAPTER 21: GLORY DAYS

He shall cover thee with his feathers, and under his wings shalt thou trust: his truth shall be thy shield and buckler. Thou shalt not be afraid for the terror by night; nor for the arrow that flieth by day; Nor for the pestilence that walketh in darkness; nor for the destruction that wasteth at noonday.

Psalm 91: 4-6

Though this passage may have been used in another area of this book, the Holy Spirit impressed upon me to reiterate it once again. I say that because a friend and I went out to eat at Glory Days restaurant in Ellicott City, Maryland, on June 16, 2020. I arrived before her and asked the waitress for a table on the inside. Mind you, the coronavirus was still in effect, but the curfew that everyone had been under was lifted.

When my friend arrived, she wanted to sit outside to get fresh air, and she still was not comfortable sitting inside. We had to compromise because I did not like to sit outside for two reasons: insects and birds flying over. Having a bad experience with a bird landing on a table near me years ago made me think twice about sitting outside eating. However, I decided to sit outside anyways.

As we indulged in a great meal, we began to talk about the Holy Spirit and things that the Holy Spirit had shown me over the past few months. Most of them came from the sky. As I spoke about these things, I could tell how she was being touched. Though she did not need to be reminded how great God is, she told me that it really reassured her confidence in what she was doing in the Body of Christ.

When the waitress came back with the check, Prophetess Pamela and I sat for roughly another thirty minutes talking about a few things until I told her, "Get up, but do not turn around!" She was a bit startled because it was so abrupt. Pam got up and then turned around, looking towards the sky. Suddenly, a large black bird flapped its wings on the table adjacent to us, and we both cut out of there fast. I told her loudly, "And that is why I don't like to sit outside and eat!"

We laughed about it along with another lady that was sitting in her car watching the event as it unfolded in front of her. The black bird pounced around the table, grabbed a piece of the sandwich left behind, and flew away. Sometimes, warning signs are all around us and, if we are not careful, they may appear after it is too late. Second Timothy 1:7 says, "For God hath not given us the spirit of fear, but of power, and of love, and of a sound mind."

Standing at my car, Pam and I talked about what was going on in the world and how God was showing His signs and wonders through the sky. I reminded her that, since October 2019, I had been speaking to her about paying attention to what was happening in the sky. I noticed that the sky was starting to look different, and I believed something big was going to take place. I also reminded her that winter was not a "real winter" in 2019/2020, and, suddenly, this plague from the Bible was upon us. As I spoke to her, witnessing what God was showing me, I told her to look at the sky. At that point, a huge rabbit appeared in the sky. I took a picture of it. She stood there and said, "It does look like a rabbit." I told her that the Holy Spirit wants us to be mindful of the phenomena taking place around us and to document what we see, whether on paper or by taking pictures, so that, when we tell others about them, they will not think we have lost our minds.

Then, the most amazing thing happened. As I continued to speak to her about the Holy Spirit, I kept telling her that it looked as though it was going to storm. Mind you, the sun had not shined since we had stood by my car to talk. The Holy Spirit told me to turn around and say this, "See, like I've been telling you before, I am able to look into the sun, and it won't hurt my eyes. Look, I am looking into the sun, and I am seeing a long, shining beam coming down." I removed my eyes from the sun and, immediately, it went back into the clouds.

Seeing this, Pam fell into amazement. The look she gave me let me know that she truly believed what I had been telling her. At that point, I saw yellow lights leading from the back of her legs and making a pathway to the sky. I told her that me looking into the sun was for her this time. God wanted her to see His glory, and the yellow lights I was seeing symbolized Him telling her not to be afraid. He had his angels protecting her.

Pam and I returned to our cars. I left immediately after praying but, little did I know, Prophetess Pamela stayed behind for approximately twenty minutes. She told me that she was so engulfed in the spirit after what had just happened that she could not help but give God the praise. You see, when we reverence God, He will let others see the miracles that He can perform through us. It amazes me to this day how God uses me to reach others, but I am so grateful that God chose me to be a witness to those that will listen.

Donna Hodges

CHAPTER 22: GO INTO THE WORLD

Mark 16:15: "And Jesus said unto them, Go ye into all the world, and preach the gospel to every creature."

Initially, when I got saved as a child, many people did not want to hear what I had to say. I would speak about how God changed my life while attending First Pentecostal Church in Pensacola, Florida. I was so determined for everyone to hear how God changed my life that they literally went in the other direction when they saw me coming. When God uses us to testify or witness for Him, the devil will try everything in his might to discourage our faith and belief in Him.

I remember when I was eight and filled with the Holy Ghost, word got around, and people laughed at me. We were at children's church in the early 70s, and our children's church leaders were showing a movie called *The Burning Hell*. I saw people standing around an open pit of fire, and their flesh was falling off their bodies. I was terrified. I began crying, and all of a sudden, the Holy Spirit took control of my body, and I began speaking in another language that I did not know. One of the leaders said, "I believe she has the Holy Ghost, and she's speaking in tongues." It was the first time I had heard about speaking in tongues.

As I got older, I continued to attend sanctified churches or Pentecostal churches because I believed that was where my true faith lives. Though I was still learning, I was even more eager to learn about how the Holy Spirit came into my body that day and changed my life forever. The older I got, the more I spoke about Christ and how He saved me. God wants to use us as His disciples so we can reach out to a world that has been dying since He created it. He told His disciples to go out and make disciples of men. He wants us to be able to touch a sick person and heal their body through faith. Matthew 28:19,

> Go therefore and make disciples of all nations, baptizing them in the name of the Father and of the Son and of the Holy Spirit, teaching them to observe all things that I have commanded you; and lo, I am with you always, even to the end of the age.
>
> Amen.

Affirming this Scripture from God, He reminds me of how He has used me to be one of His disciples through many visions, dreams, healings, and teachings. As far back as I can remember as a teenager, I prophesized to my mother about seeing her dead mother, who I had never met. Her eyes being closed, her skin radiantly dark, and her eyes sunk back in her head. At the time, I was overcome by fear because I did not know who I was seeing in these visions. Two days later, my mother's brother went home to be with the Lord, and he was calling on his mother. Many other times, I received calls about someone on their death bed, and the Holy Spirit instructed me what to tell them so that the person would live.

As a woman of God, I have been a teacher of His Word, ministering to my family, friends, strangers in the store and, at times, standing behind the pulpit. I never knew what power God had instilled in me until I came to Maryland and God put me back in touch with the church I attended while serving in the Navy. In 1991, no one showed me how to be a disciple of Christ, but I began learning while attending Full Gospel Emancipation Church in Severn, MD. Seeing how the Holy Spirit touched the lives of individuals in that church helped me to understand where I stood in Christ. It made me a believer in the spirit and a speaker of many tongues.

Being in the military, you travel to many places, and I was eventually stationed in Fort Gordon, Georgia. The church I attended there, I attended for all the wrong reasons. It was not of the faith that I had just come from, but it was something me and my family could attend together. The Word was spoken differently, and the people did not have the agape love for their pastor the way they mine did at Full Gospel Emancipation Church. Since then, the name "Full Gospel Emancipation Church" has been changed to River of Life Worship Center.

In January 2016, I moved back to Maryland from Georgia. I tried going back to a church that I left in 2003, but the message was not the same, and neither were the people. I kept seeing another church from a distance, off Route 32, but never knew how to get to it from Telegraph Road. Then, one day, the Holy Spirit pointed it out to me. There were barriers leading through the woods and an arrow pointing to the end of the road. As I drove to the end of the road, I was determined to make it to worship service. To find such a church is to find the Holy Spirit, agape love, and the Word of God.

There is a saying at River of Life Worship Center: "Once you attend this church, your life will never be the same." They were absolutely right.

I had been attending River of Life Worship Center since 2016, and my life has never been the same since that day. The Spirit of God is in that place. Seeing the Holy Spirit on several occasions and being ministered to by the vessels of God has shown me what true discipleship means in the Body of Christ. Not only have I been able to see the Holy Spirit, but I have been able to touch and heal those that were sick back in Georgia, Florida, and even here in Maryland. God points out those He wants me to pray for because He knows that they will receive His message and accept their healing. I have spoken to the unsaved and delivered them from their old way of life. I have dreamed dreams that have come true and interpreted other people's dreams. I have spoken about things before they happened and within minutes of me speaking, they happened. There are so many things God has shown me as His disciple, but He would not use me until I was completely focused on Him and His Word. I am the first to tell anyone I am not a prophetess but a messenger of Christ. Though I may be able to see things others cannot, until God calls me a prophetess, I will be His messenger.

Being a disciple of Christ is not an easy task. The devil

will come at you in many ways, and you must be prepared when he comes. First Corinthians 15:58 tells us, "Therefore, my beloved brethren, be ye steadfast, unmovable, always abounding in the work of the Lord, forasmuch as ye know that your labour is not in vain in the Lord."

In order for us to defeat the devil, we have to put on the whole armor of God that ye may be able to stand against the wiles of the devil. When we do this, we will be able to stand against anything the devil brings our way. The whole armor of God includes:

(1) **Put on the Breastplate of Righteousness:** Ephesians 6:14 says, "Stand therefore, having your loins girt about with truth, and having on the breastplate of righteousness."

(2) **Taking the Shield of Faith:** Ephesians 6:16 says, "Above all, taking the shield of faith, wherewith ye shall be able to quench all the fiery darts of the wicked."

(3) **Take the Helmet of Salvation and the Sword of the Spirit:** Ephesians 6:17-20 says,

Which is the word of God: Praying always with all prayer and supplication in the Spirit, and watching thereunto with all perseverance and supplication for all saints; And for me, that utterance may be given unto me, that I may open my mouth boldly, to make known the mystery of the gospel, For which I am an ambassador in bonds: that therein I may speak boldly, as I ought to speak.

God is saying to us that He will be our protector when trouble arrives, and He will never leave us, nor will He forsake us. He will guide us through the hard times and through any sickness that may come upon us. When we leave this world, we can rest assured that we will see Him in heaven.

Donna Hodges

CHAPTER 23: AND GIANTS WILL FALL

Ecclesiastes 6:2: "A man to whom God hath given riches, wealth, and honour, so that he wanteth nothing for his soul of all that he desireth, yet God giveth him not power to eat thereof, but a stranger eateth it: this is vanity, and it is an evil disease."

In our world today, after the sudden impact of the coronavirus, businesses have shut down, the stock market is like a roller coaster, and hundreds of thousands of lives have been lost. The substantial loss of jobs and the shutting down of sports (such as the NBA, MLB, and NFL), concerts, movie theatres, and many other businesses have devastated the world economy. There are those who thought they were on top of the world but are now watching everything they have gained crumble. Mark 8:36: "For what shall it profit a man, if he shall gain the whole world, and lose his own soul?"

A powerful, seemingly invincible man once said that he was equal to God but has now been shut down by God Almighty. Mongols and giants have fallen because they put their trust in idols and not God. God says in Ecclesiastes 2:22, "For what hath man of all his labour, and of the vexation of his heart, wherein he hath laboured under the sun?" The material things you desire are meaningless to God and are desired in vain.

From child molesters to rapists to murderers, even to the highest positions in the world, God has claimed victory over their strongholds, and their kingdoms are crashing down before their own eyes. We must bow down to our God. God has stricken their jobs, their businesses, and their families. The ones who have mistreated women and children their entire lives are seeing the backlashes of life suddenly caught up with them. God sees everything, and what is done in the dark shall come to light. God said in Luke 12:2-3,

> For there is nothing covered, that shall not be revealed; neither hid, that shall not be known. Therefore, whatsoever ye have spoken in darkness shall be heard in the light; and that which ye have spoken in the ear in closets shall be proclaimed upon

the housetops.

These so-called giants are reaping the punishments they have inflicted upon others, and their judgment day has finally come. Most are either serving time in prison or losing their empires, homes, or families. Some have even taken their own lives. They just cannot take the pressure of losing everything. Have they even considered the people that have nothing? These people find a way to survive. God provides for the wants and needs of those that cannot provide for themselves.

Others believed that the empires they inherited from their fathers and mothers would last forever. God does not promise us the materialistic things we have will last forever. God promises us eternal life through His Son, Jesus Christ.

When God stepped in to tear down these so-called "giants," their lives shifted and started to crumble. They idolized their worldly possessions. They were too proud to give God the praise for their accomplishments. However, there is a handful of people that give to the poor, but most of them selfishly will not give to their own families. God said, "You cannot worship man and Him too." And yet, no one has given thought to what God is trying to say. Everyone is so caught up in what they have lost or how to make it from day to day that they completely forgot how to pray and ask God for help. God said in John 10:27-28, "My sheep hear my voice and I know them and they follow; And I give unto them eternal life; and they shall never perish, neither shall any man." If we make ourselves known to God, God will make Himself known to us.

Have you thought about the things that we take for granted that God has given us? Waking up is the biggest blessing God has given us besides His Son's life. But somehow, we tend to idolize material things more than we praise God. We forgot about our souls, and this has caused God to remind us that He can take our material things away just as fast as He gave them to us.

Think about it! Every year, there is an expectancy of seeing the NBA playoffs; the first pitch of the MLB being cast by the president of the United States; the master's in Augusta being played by the top contenders; the excitement of seeing who will conquer Wimbledon, the Australian or the US Open in 2020; the attendance of the Grammys, Emmys, and many other awards shows to see who won what award and who had the best dress. We eagerly await the latest Hollywood movies that will hit the theater, the NFL/NBA drafts from the top perspective players in the game, and even those who attended church on Resurrection Sunday. Yet, when it comes to attending church or giving God the praise, we make excuses. Crickets can be heard chirping outside the windows.

Many people who have become champions and awardees have allowed greed to become a factor and demand more than what they are worth. Psalm 49:16-19 says,

> Be not thou afraid when one is made rich, when the glory of his house is increased; For when he dieth he shall carry nothing away: his glory shall not descend after him. Though while he lived, he blessed his soul: and men will praise thee, when thou doest well to thyself. He shall go to the generation of his fathers; they shall never see light. Man, that is in honour and understandeth not, is like the beasts that perish.

God has allowed them to come back from illnesses and the birth of their children to win titles. And yet, they let greed get in the way. Their kingdom started to crumble, and even those in the music and movie industries have allowed their bodies to be temples of the world instead of temples of God. Staying at home and appreciating what God blessed them with was not good enough for them. They chose to go into the world out of greed for popularity. God had to shut it all down to show the world that He is and always will be in control.

Again, "What profits a man to gain the whole world but lose his soul?"

When we deny God, we have to face the consequences. Therefore, at the beginning of 2020, God said, "Enough!" He is tired of it all. He, not China nor any other man, showed the world that one way or another, you will bow down and worship Him. Man worshipped and idolized worldly things for so long that God decided to show man that if you put your trust in man, He will flee from you. People call this the "Invisible Virus" and the "Chinese Virus." There is nothing invisible about it. God is the only one that can stop the entire world at once without receiving credit. Man is so afraid to come to terms that we are living in the last days and that the plagues of Exodus and Revelation are upon us. Blame has been placed on China because it's easier to blame someone in power. If our leaders knew God and the powers of God, they would see that the powers of the Lord are upon us. Then, they would lead our country the way leaders are supposed to.

Think about it. Is it really possible for such an outbreak of a virus from China to conquer the entire world all at once? It's not possible. Only God can cause such a tremendous event to happen. And He is not finished. God's first commandment is "Thou shalt have NO other gods before me" (Exodus 20:3).

So why do we put all these things before God? Simply spoken, man has worshipped idols and other men for so long and placed God on the backburner that he takes God for granted. He thinks God will always answer their prayers if they ask because the Bible says so. However, God will answer prayers when He sees it fits and not at man's will. When God's name is mentioned to the younger generation, it means nothing to them because they were not taught to worship God. They were told, "God does not exist. Or the world is based on science and evolution, not God. That's how things were created." Man has corrupted God's world so much that many kill themselves trying to get away from it.

The Bible also speaks of a person that seeks greed in such a way that they would go so far as to move in with their elderly parents and wait for them to die. God tells them in Proverbs 20:20-21 that "Whoso curseth his father or his mother, his lamp shall be put out in obscure darkness. An inheritance may be gotten hastily at the begin; but the end thereof shall not be blessed." Things that are gained unjustly will not last. Idolizing money over God only leads to destruction in the end.

It has been said by Solomon in Proverbs 21:20, "There

is treasure to be desired and oil in the dwelling of the wise, but a foolish man spendeth it up." A wise man saves for his future while a foolish man spends whatever he has on things he does not need.

A young rich man once asked Jesus in Matthew 19:16-24, "What good thing shall I do, that I may have eternal life?" Jesus told him to keep His commandments. The young man replied, "All these things have I kept from my youth up; what lack I yet?" Jesus said unto him, "If thou wilt be perfect, go and sell that thou hast and feed the poor and thou shall have treasure in heaven and come and follow me." But when the young man heard that, he went away sorrowful because he had great possessions. Then said Jesus unto His disciples, "Verily I say unto you, that a rich man shall hardly enter into the kingdom of Heaven. And again, I say unto you, it is easier for a camel to go through the eye o f a needle that for a rich man to enter into the kingdom of God."

We see this as evidence in the world today. Man has gained so much prosperity in life that they have forgotten about the people who gave them power. Not only that, but they have also forgotten to acknowledge Christ. Some will walk by a beggar in the streets and look down upon him, while those who have the least will give to the beggar. They will say in their mind, *He needs to get a job and stop begging.* But they may not know the circumstances of this individual. This could have been a person just like themselves but fell hard on their luck.

Witnessing this pandemic, I have learned many things about our government, our churches, those that have gained, and those that have not. Some are willing to help, but others are afraid of contracting the virus, so they stay in their homes watching from afar, hoping that it will soon pass so they can get their lives back. Tomorrow is not promised to anyone. I have always had this slogan for myself, "Live today like tomorrow will never come." If there are things that need to be done today like giving God the praise, helping others, gathering food, or taking a long walk, I will do it because I never know what tomorrow may bring. Now, in the aftermath of this pandemic, my slogan is "Forget about yesterday, strive for today, and pray for tomorrow."

Many people are sitting in their homes worried about paying their next bill, losing their jobs, and putting food on the table. There are others that have gained prosperity hoarding what they have instead of feeding God's sheep. For many have said, "Lord Lord," but only a few will be chosen. It is my philosophy that if I ever gained prosperity, I would take what I have gained and go to the poorest of neighborhoods and feed God's sheep. Even now, I use what I have during the Christmas season. The Holy Spirit told me to get twenty cards and fill them with blessings. Then, He took me through the poorest neighborhoods and pointed out His sheep that He wanted me to bless. This is how God wants us to feed His sheep.

I recently spoke to a young lady that served in the military who left seeking bigger opportunities. These opportunities took her around the world to Japan and other places paying top dollar. However, she did not believe in God! She told me, "there was no God." Her life started to change. God had given her a great job in the intelligence field, but greed set in, and she wanted more. She thought because she was making top dollar, that she had to have the finest house, car, and clothes. While working as a contractor, she did not see the bullet that was about to strike her. Her husband, the man she had given her life to and conceived a child with, was working hard to steal everything from her accounts. If she changed her bank card, he would be waiting at the mailbox for the next one to arrive and take it from her. She chose to worship the devil and his followers, and her husband robbed her of everything that she had. As I tried ministering to this young lady on Friday, April 17, 2020, telling her about the goodness of God, her response to me was, "If I did not believe in God before this pandemic, I sure do not believe in Him now." Then, she said, "Why would I put my trust in God when things like this are happening to people?"

At that point, I knew my ministry to her would need some time. I began by saying, "God loves you, and He wants you to come to Him. He knows what you need and when you need it. He just wants you to ask Him for it. God will give you the desires of your heart if you prayed to Him and asked for it." Although applying for hundreds of jobs with a Master's degree in cybersecurity should have gotten it for her, some things worked against her. She definitely needed Christ in her life.

Then, I told her about how would God allowed me to gaze into the sun on two different occasions and revealed things to me. Afterward, I told her about the many revelations God had shown me since I was a child. This conversation lasted for roughly fifteen minutes. I am not sure if I was able to reach her but, at least she knows that God loves her and wants her to come back to Him.

REMEMBER: The same person you pass by in the streets might be the one individual that comes to your rescue. For you hear the slogan, "Make America Great Again!" The one and only time the world was great was when God created the heavens and the earth. Once man entered the world, sin was upon them, and they began to destroy all that God had created. We have never lived in a great world because, if it were so great, there would not have been slaves, racism, idol worshippers, adulterers, liars, cheaters, transgenders, homosexuality, police brutality against men and women, and many other things that are not of God. God did not create us to be this way, but man changed what God created. For this, many will suffer. Not one amongst us is pure, and we will all be judged on the day we see Christ. We will never live in a perfect world because, on earth, there is no perfection according to God.

CHAPTER 24: WARNING FROM THE SPIRIT

Acts 2:17: "And it shall come to pass in the last days, saith God, I will pour out of my Spirit upon all flesh: and your sons and your daughters shall prophesy, and your young men shall see visions, and your old men shall dream dreams."

When we are visited in our dreams by the Holy Spirit, sometimes it may not be pleasant, but we have to accept what the Spirit of the Lord is saying to us and pray for its meaning. You may be deep into a dream that only you and God know about. They are messages from the Holy Spirit letting you know that something is about to take place. Sometimes, they can be downright scary. Many times, my mother (who has been deceased since January 2002) will visit me briefly in my dreams. It depends, though. If she smiles, I know she is telling me someone very close to me will pass on soon. If she says nothing, it is a warning that something is happening within the family back home, and I need to check on them.

My latest dream about my mother was on March 23, 2020. We were at a church service, and my mother was laughing. Suddenly, she fell to the floor and died. I sat for a few seconds gasping for air. Then, I started screaming for help. But when the paramedics got ready to pick her up on the stretcher, instead, they picked up a little boy who turned his head and smiled at me.

My alarm clock went off, and I never had the opportunity to finish the dream. Two days later, I received a call from my cousin telling me that her oldest brother's grandson had been shot and killed.

My mother knew that I was close to him and warned me in my dream before it took place. Throughout the years, I have documented my dreams as I saw them. Dreams that got away visited me later in life when something happened, and there was no proof of me ever seeing them. When God was fed up with man, he told Noah to build an ark in Genesis 6 after warning him that He was going to destroy the earth. This is happening now. God is once again fed up with man, and He is giving His prophets, prophetesses, and others charge to warn man that He is coming very soon.

When we take into consideration the things, such as dreams and visions, that God has shown us, we need to realize that we are seers of the Spirit. God has chosen a few to prophesize and witness to others. Having the ability to see things or prophesize does not mean we are perfect. It just means that God has vessels on earth to help us get back to Him. He placed us here for those reasons. He wants us to minister to others and let them know that time on earth is short, but eternal life with Him lasts forever. Jesus said in Matthew 20:28, "Even as the Son of man came not to be ministered unto, but to minister and to give his life a ransom for many."

Donna Hodges

CHAPTER 25: DELIVERED BY THE SPIRIT

Isaiah 43:18-19 (NIV): "Forget the former things; do not dwell on the past. See, I am doing a new thing! Now it springs up; do you not perceive it? I am making a way in the wilderness and streams in the wastelands."

When I woke up on April 17, 2020, the Holy Spirit had me go to the mirror and look at myself. I did not understand the meaning of it. But, as I began to look at myself, I could finally see that God had molded me into a vessel, a disciple, and a messenger of Christ. I did not see the low self-esteem little girl, but I saw a beautiful lady blossomed by the grace of God being renewed by His grace and mercy. My hair or the way I looked was no longer an issue for me because it was how God wanted me to be.

God showed me that as I was growing up. I had been so

caught up in my hair and the way I looked that I had forgotten why He was using me as a testimony of faith. God delivered me from the spirit of conceit. Although I did not see myself as conceited, always caring about my appearance is a form of being conceited. I had been so naive to think that men would be attracted to me if I had long hair and a beautiful face. Then, I remembered, in the eyes of the Lord, all His children are beautiful. He created us in His image, so we must look good. That was enough for me to not concentrate on the way I looked to men but to be accountable to how God perceived me. It did not matter anymore whether my hair was long or my face had a few impurities; what mattered was the change that God had brought me through and how God was using me to be a witness to others.

God wants us to stay in His will and not get caught up in worldly things.

CHAPTER 26: THE SPIRIT THAT DWELLETH IN ME

Romans 8:11: "But if the Spirit of him that raised up Jesus from the dead dwell in you, he that raised up Christ from the dead shall also quicken your mortal bodies by his Spirit that dwelleth in you."

In the summer of 2019, I purchased a prayer cloth from my church and began reading the printed Scriptures. I started taking the cloth to work and leaving it on my desk. It seemed like I was inundated with so many deaths, sicknesses, and evil spirits that I wanted to keep Scriptures near me so I could stay encouraged. As I read these Scriptures, I believed God would take away the sadness in my heart and give me reasons to rejoice. I had no idea what the significance of this cloth was until I began reading Scriptures in their entirety.

On April 19, 2020, I woke up to several different dreams

to include one of my former first ladies from First Shiloh Baptist Church with a message to her husband. Unfortunately, by the time I woke up, I could not remember her message. So, I went into the living room and grabbed my Bible to read God's Word. He led me to Jeremiah 1 and told me that I would be studying this chapter. I began reading and trying to understand what the Holy Spirit was telling me. After turning on the TV, I noticed that CNN was blocked. All the other channels were on but, for some reason, their network was down.

Again, I got caught up in the appearance of my hair. All I could see was what it used to look like and how it is now. But then the Holy Spirit stepped in and said, "Focus on what God has you to do. Your hair is a material thing that God can and will restore. But you must put your trust in Him. Satan is trying to deter you from what God has assigned and instructed you to do." So instead of going to the bathroom to check on my hair and what it looked like for the fifteenth time this morning, the Holy Spirit led me to my spare room, where I do all my writings. Not being able to attend church and worship God was starting to lead me into depression. I had to find something that would occupy my time.

When I got to the spare room, I noticed the prayer cloth

that I had purchased lying on the bed. Since the coronavirus had everyone on restriction, I brought it home and left it in my bedroom. However, the night before, the Holy Spirit had me bring it from my bedroom to the spare room. I had no idea why, but I followed His instructions. And as I stood over this cloth looking at the Scriptures and the prayer printed in the center, I began reading each one of them. It wasn't until I reached the fourth verse that the Holy Spirit started making my eyes see what was happening.

Romans 8:32 says, "He that spared not his own Son, but delivered him up for us all, how shall he not with him also freely give us all things?" Meaning, God gave us Jesus. Therefore, I know He gives me every good thing. Engaged thoroughly in each Scripture, I read and prayed. I did this until I reached the one Scripture that God so clearly pointed out to me (Romans 8:11). At the end of that verse, the words "Spirit that Dwelleth in you" set my entire soul on fire, and the Spirit of God came upon me. My spirit poured out in praise, in tongues, rejoicing at what God had been preparing me for. This was the moment that I could say this novel is of God and about the *Spirit That Dwells in Me,* that I am a testament of His love, His visions, His truth. That I was truly chosen as

He told me on March 22, 2020, the day I stood looking at the sun that I would be the one to document these things for many generations to come, to speak about the miracles that I have seen Him perform, and that I would forever be a witness for His Son.

God chose me and many other disciples, prophets, prophetesses, pastors, rabbis, and ministers to go forth as evidence of things to come and things that are not seen. He chose us to teach the world of His goodness and show them the revelations of Jesus Christ. We are the true witnesses that God exists, and the Spirit of God dwells in our spirit.

CHAPTER 27: ALIGNMENT
OF THE SAINTS

For the perfecting of the saints, for the work of the
ministry, for the edifying of the body of Christ: Till we
all come in the unity of the faith and of the knowledge
of the Son of God, unto a perfect man, unto the
measure of the stature of the fulness of Christ. That
we henceforth be no more children, tossed to and fro,
and carried about with every wind of doctrine, by the
sleight of men, and cunning craftiness, whereby they
lie in wait to deceive.

Ephesians 4:12-13

Aligning ourselves with the Word of God gives us a
spiritual alignment with one another. If one of God's children
is out of alignment with Christ, it has a reflection on the others.
Jesus chose His disciples one by one and asked them to follow
Him. They left their lives behind and followed Jesus because

they wanted to listen to what He had to say. Peter and John were close to Him, and it seemed, at times, the others were a little skeptical. They wanted to know more about Jesus, but Peter and John believed who Jesus was. When Jesus died, it was Thomas that had false hopes. He did not believe that Jesus had risen from the dead. He had to touch and see with his own eyes. Jesus told him to touch His side and see the scars in His hands from where He hung on the cross.

If we do not believe that Jesus died for us, how can we align ourselves as saints? The world is not going to get any better. Saints of God must find a way to align ourselves with the Word of God. We cannot go out and change what God has written for self-glorification. God gave us a Word to study, but many have changed it for their glorification and understanding. God said so Himself in Revelation 22:18-19,

> For I testify unto every man that heareth the words of the prophecy of this book. If any man shall add unto these things, God shall add unto him the plagues that are written in this book: And if any man shall take away from the words of the book of this prophecy, God shall take away his part out of the book of life, and out of the holy city, and from the things which are written in this book.

Men try to interpret what the Bible is saying with their own words by creating a Bible to simplify or make beautiful, as I have heard some preachers say what was originally written. They are not doing it for the glorification of God, but they are doing it to please man and their own wealth. When man is out of alignment with the saints, He is out of alignment with God, and greed takes over. For some, it is easy to read the rewritten versions in the NKJV, MSG, NASB, ESV, PASSION, NIV, and many others. But if God wanted His words rewritten, He would have told you. Just like the way the Holy Spirit is writing this for you, if someone came back and rewrote what the Holy Spirit has said in this book, it would be a fraud. The only part of this book that is written by me is when I talk about myself. Then, the Holy Spirit intervenes and takes over.

If we are to be warriors of Christ, we must align ourselves with His original Word and teach the prophecies as they were written, not the new versions that man interpreted from the Bible, but the original Word of God found in the King James Version.

CHAPTER 28: RUNNING MAN OVER PYRAMID HOUSE

And he said unto me, Thou must prophesy again before many peoples, and nations, and tongues, and kings. And there was given me a reed like a rod; and the angel stood, saying, Rise, and measure the temple of God, and the altar, and them that worship therein.

Revelation 10:11, 11:1

The Holy Spirit said unto me, "Wake up, my child!" I immediately arose as I heard these words utter to me. A glaring bright light was shining in my eyes through my windowpane. I knew the Holy Spirit had awoken me to see the brightness of the moon. It was 1:28 a.m. on Wednesday morning, July 1, 2020. The moon was brightly shining through the white blinds of my bedroom window. I immediately grabbed my cellphone.

One thing I knew for sure was if the Holy Spirit woke me up, He wanted me to see something.

As my husband slept soundly next to me, I got up and peeped through the white shades. The beautiful sight that I saw in the sky was unimaginable. What appeared to be a dark cloud on the side of the moon turned out to be something totally different. As I aimed my camera in the direction of the moon, I had no idea what I was about to capture. But I saw nothing—only a cloud.

First, there was a bright moon with a dark cloud. Then, the second picture had a slight glare in the background that I could barely make out. But, when the Holy Spirit told me to zoom in, what I saw next gave me chills. A man appeared to be running and pointing at the moon next to a pyramid. However, it was my neighbor's rooftop in the shape of a pyramid. I was in complete awe of God.

What kind of love did He have for me to show me such beauty at 1:28 a.m.? God had been revealing so many things to me, and sometimes I wondered if I was even worthy of them.

I kept asking myself: *What is God trying to reveal to me with all these signs and wonders He has shown me?* According to the four signs of the apocalypse, in the book of

Revelation, we can find the symbolization of evil to come. What is meant by this is that God is preparing us for the big war that is getting ready to take place, and those that are ready will be caught up into glory and rest with Him. But those that are not will be cast into the open flames of darkness forever.

The four signs of the apocalypse are: a white horse in which a figure representing Conquest will ride; War is on the red horse, Famine rides on the black horse, and the pale horse carries the plagues. The first horseman is the Antichrist, a global war which we already seem to be heading towards is the second horseman, an economic collapse is the third horseman, and one-quarter of the world's population will die from plagues.

As most of these signs are coming to pass, I ask myself, *How prepared am I for the arrival of the rapture?* The answer to this question is, *I believe that deep inside of me, if the rapture came right now, I am ready.* God had been preparing me since I was a child. However, for the past couple of years, God has really shown me His signs and wonders, and I have done my best to warn those that would listen. Many laughed when I tried to tell them that something was going on in the sky in October 2019. Some said, "It does look kind of strange," but no one really paid attention except me. I could not help but pay attention because every time I turned around, the Holy Spirit was whispering in my ears.

You see, the Holy Spirit chose me because He knew without a doubt that I loved to talk and witness to people about God's greatness. This is what the Holy Spirit woke me up to on Wednesday morning at 1:28 a.m. Our God is an amazing God!

CHAPTER 29: SATAN THOUGHT HE HAD ME

And the seventy returned again with joy, saying, Lord, even the devils are subject unto us through thy name. And Jesus said unto them, I beheld Satan as lightning fall from heaven. Behold, I give unto you power to tread on serpents and scorpions, and over all the power of the enemy: and nothing shall by any means hurt you.

Luke 10:17-19

While speaking with a spiritual advisor of mine, I realized that all my life Satan had been out of destroying me and trying to hinder the revelations that God put forth in my life.

From the earlier years of my life, the devil chased me and thought, *I finally got her.* But he did not realize that no one can contain a child of God. Every situation he could put me in, God turned it around for betterment. God knew that I loved telling people how He saved me from being molested when I was six by an old white man while raking his yard, so I could tell the world about it. He knew that when my mother asked me to light a cigarette for her, my pajamas would catch on fire. He knew that while playing an innocent game of "Hide and Seek," I would be locked in an old refrigerator and live to tell the story. He knew that while friends were swinging on a clothesline pole, the pole would give way and bust my head open, and I would live to tell it. God knew that when I married my first husband, he would snap my back and rape me two days later. But I lived to tell it. God knew that through all my trials and tribulations, I would tell of His goodness and how He saved me from whatever Satan threw my way. You see, when Satan thought he had me, *I got away!*

When we reverence God, He blesses us. I have no problem testifying to man, woman, boy, or girl about God's goodness.

Honestly, how many people have lived to talk about the things God brought them through and serve as a witness to others about it? People do not witness to others about God because they are afraid of how it may look.

I often tell people, "Before there was a 'Me Too' movement, there was a 'Me.'" Imagine doing something as innocent as raking someone's yard for seventy-five cents and having an old white man grab your private part! Many children lose their minds over things like that, and it did haunt me for years because I believed he was always coming to get me. I had nightmares for years. And though I told my mother and anyone who would listen, back then, they just swept it under the rug and told me to keep my mouth shut. You had to be strong. What did not kill me made me stronger in the Word of God! It gave me something to testify about. It allowed me to go places and witness to others that had been abused and to tell them how I made it through. It was nobody but God and the Holy Spirit dwelling inside of me.

In the early '70s, I watched a movie at First Assembly of God Church in Pensacola, FL, called *The Burning Hell*. Now, I do not know about you, but who shows such a movie to kids in elementary school? It was enough to scare the bejesus out of you. That is exactly what it did to me. It terrified me. But the awesome thing about seeing that movie was that I received the Holy Ghost and the Holy Spirit. Satan thought he had me by trying to scare the wits out of me but, instead, I gained salvation, and it has guided me my entire life. When I was downtrodden, God gave me strength. When I was weak, God made me strong. When I was bound, God loosened my shackles and set me free. Every time Satan tried to destroy me, God was there to intervene. I can almost hear God telling Satan, "No, Satan! That one is mine." Glory to God! Hallelujah!

Even as I am writing this chapter, Satan tried to interfere. I was trying to get the chapters to align with how the Holy Spirit wanted me to deliver it to you, but I accidently deleted His work—*gone!* Two whole pages were inadvertently deleted. I sat for minutes, covering my face in complete disbelief. How could I be so distracted and forget that fast? For the life of me, I could not remember a single thing that was written. I was devastated.

Then, the Holy Spirit said unto me, "Focus, Donna! Breathe!"

But I could not. Pages of hard work were gone.

The Holy Spirit whispered in my ear again, "Focus and breathe!"

I looked at the computer—completely distraught. I saved my work and called my husband, who was in Georgia at the time. By the time I kept repeating what had happened and, suddenly, the Holy Spirit brought back my erased memory. I told my husband that I had to go!

This time, I grabbed my notebook and pen and sat down to write. God brought back my memory with added information that I did not have while I was typing.

Satan thought he had me, but I got away!

CHAPTER 30: A LIFE RETURNED

Numbers 11:25: "And the Lord came down in a cloud, and spake unto him, and took of the spirit that was upon him, and gave it unto the seventy elders: and it came to pass, that when the spirit rested upon them, they prophesied and did not cease."

The prophecy of a woman taking control of the life she once had through the power of the Spirit that dwells in her shows strength and encouragement to those that never knew how to rely on God. When the Holy Spirit sets His sight on you, you will have the power to cast out demons within yourself and others. God gives you the ultimate power to pray over those that He appoints you to pray over, and He gives you the power of prophecy through His Son, Jesus Christ. I am in awe of the things the Holy Spirit has revealed to me, and I do not take them lightly. As the Holy Spirit prophesied to me, He will allow me to share things with others that are to come and that forever will be.

On Saturday, April 18, 2020, as I peacefully showered, amazing thoughts encountered my mind, and I embraced every drop of water falling upon my body and my hair. I thought about life and all the things God has allowed me to do and what the devil had tricked me into doing.

As the soap suds ran down my body and I got ready to rinse the shampoo from my depleting hair, I could feel something—a spirit whispering in my ear. My heart began to pound, and my mouth opened in praise. A song by gospel artist Be Be Winans, "In Harm's Way," danced on my tongue. I began to lift the name of Jesus.

I heard the Holy Spirit say, "Your hair will return at its fullest, and this is how!" I stopped short of my praise and listened. I thought I was done with worrying about my hair. But God was reassuring me of His promise that He was going to take care of it. Before, I tried doing things my way. But this time, the Holy Spirit was lending me His hand. The Holy Spirit directed me to wash and condition my hair twice a week, but (instead of blow-drying and hot curling like I usually do) He reminded me that, as a child, I did not have a blow dryer or a hot curler. Instead, I washed my hair and greased it with oil or hair grease while it was still wet. It made my hair long and healthy but, as I got older, I started to change it by putting chemicals such as perms and dyes in it, which caused a lot of breakage.

Tears began to fall. *All this time,* I thought, *all I needed to do was return to the way I did things as a child and let God handle the rest.* Matthew 18:3 says, "And verily I said unto you, except ye be converted and become as a child, ye shall not enter into the kingdom of Heaven."

It made perfect sense. When I was a child, I dwelled on things that I could not change and, as I got older, they followed me through adulthood. The Lord showed me that it was not about my hair, my looks, or the things of the past, but it is about the Word of God and the Spirit that dwells in me—His Spirit. He had been placing His love in my heart for over fifty-three years.

For so long, I have helped others in ways that I did not know I could. I remember praying for God to bless me so that I could one day be able to help those that were less fortunate than me. When we bless others, God will pour out blessings upon blessings on us. The Lord said in Psalm 132:15, "I will abundantly bless her provision: I will satisfy her poor with bread."

Financially, I did not have much. But what little I had, I shared with the homeless, my family, and my friends. I never expected anything in return, but God gave it to me anyway—His Son and the Holy Spirit. But when it came to me, I fell short. I allowed low self-esteem to take charge of my life. All along, God was telling me that all I needed was Him.

My entire life, I attended many churches of different denominations, but the church I was looking for was within me. The Spirit of the Lord was dwelling in me, returning my life back to the way it used to be when I worshipped Him and Him only. Now that He has brought life back to me, I am inspired to be faithful to Him and myself.

I now have the reassurance that with every effort I put forth, God will meet me with a hundred percent. God showed me how to deliver my body from pain and how to pray for those inflicted with pain in their bodies. When we put medications in our bodies, we poison our bodies and acknowledge the medications we are taking are healing us instead of believing and trusting in God. I'm not saying that we are not to take medicines because God made physicians so that they could prescribe the right ones to us. What I am trying to say is, we have to be cognizant of what we are taking in conjunction with other medicines. We poison our bodies with chemicals that are not needed. Do you not know that God is the author of healing and deliverer of pain? Trust God like I did.

As I speak, my eyes fill with tears. I often think about all the times God has been there for me and carried me through the darkest days of my life. God says, "Do not go backward thinking about what happened yesterday." But glorify Him when we are delivered. All I can do is say, "Thank you, Jesus, for saving me and returning my life back to me."

The Holy Spirit said in Deuteronomy 31:6, "Be strong and of a good courage, fear not, nor be afraid of them; for the Lord God, He it is that doth go with thee; he will not fail thee, nor forsake thee." In Matthew 28:20, it also says, "Teaching them to observe all things whatsoever I have commanded you and lo, I am with you always, even unto the end of the world. Amen."

As the Spirit of the Lord continued to speak to me, He said, "Your life is not your own. I have dwelled in you from the beginning. You have shared with many about the grace of God and how the Holy Spirit has used you." Even as I am documenting this, Satan is trying to attack me. Satan tried stopping my progress as I deliver it to you. The more I testify and witness to you about God and the Holy Spirit, the more the enemy attacks me. I am ready, though. Jesus said in 2 Corinthians 10:4-5,

> For the weapons of our warfare are not carnal, but mighty through God to the pulling down of strong holds. Casting down imaginations, and every high thing that exalteth itself against the knowledge of God and bringing into captivity every thought to be obedience of Christ.

I have put Satan on notice. I told him to flee from me. He has no dominion over me or my body. I cast him back to the pits of hell from whence he came.

And then, I continued to document what the Holy Spirit has instructed me to do. The Lord showed me that He is mightier than Satan. I do not have to fight my battles with him. Jesus died on the cross so He can fight my battles for me. When my hair fell out, my self-esteem really dropped. My hopes of regaining it failed, but God showed me a new Donna developing from the old. The old me was about my hair and the compliments I received, but the new me is all about how I can please God. Don't let who you are stop you from gaining God's favor! Focus on what God has for you and let Him return your life back to you. Now that He has shown me what to do with my hair, I can focus on what God has planned next in my life.

Donna Hodges

CHAPTER 31: DEMONS IN THE SKY

And I looked, and behold, a whirlwind came out of the north, a great cloud, and a fire infolding itself, and a brightness was about it, and out of the midst thereof as the colour of amber, out of the midst of the fire. Also out of the midst thereof came the likeness of four living creatures. And this was their appearance; they had the likeness of a man.

Ezekiel 1:4-5

The Lord said unto me on July 12, 2020, "And the demons shall devour the earth. They shall prey upon those that are weak and vulnerable. Stand strong and put on the whole armor of God and the breastplate of faith, for I have shown you many things through dreams, visions, and the sky. It is up to you to share them with the world."

I believe the demons that the Lord was referring to

are fowls of the air, Satan, and unforeseen monsters that our eyes have not beheld. Two years ago, the Lord showed me that things were changing in the atmosphere. The sky was not the same. The sun and moon were shining brighter than ever. At times, dark clouds would form, but no rain would fall.

When the months changed on the east coast, the seasons were not changing. Winters were like a cool breeze passing through the air. Every blue moon, there were drops of snowflakes, but they were not consistent. The brisk and chill of winter did not happen on the east coast, even in places like New York and Boston that were used to getting a couple of feet of snow during the winter.

Then, in October 2019, I really saw the change. At that point, I told anyone who would listen they needed to pay attention to the sky. The sky is going to tell the story of what is to come. Some listened, and some even laughed and told me, "Girl, you crazy!"

"What is your infatuation with the sky?" Another asked.

I told him, "Just look at it! It's not the same."

When the whispers of the coronavirus started to spread in January 2020, I knew God was in control. That is when God started showing me images in the sky. First, He showed me the images seen in the sun on March 22, 2020. God showed me a beautiful crystalize cross that turned into a sword, an altar made of some type of bronze with three poles, two dark images on the right side of the sun, and then, the sun went to complete darkness with a ring around it. Immediately, the sun turned into a bright yellow, and that is when the Holy Spirit said, "Look upon the earth!"

Everywhere I looked, yellow lights were there. The Holy Spirit said unto, "These are the angels that I have placed upon the earth to watch over you."

Lately, God has shown me images that were not so pleasant and allowed me to capture some from the sky to show the world. A really frightening image came while I was on an airplane heading to Baltimore, MD, from Augusta, GA. Imagine watching TV on your phone, and suddenly the Holy Spirit says, "Look out the window!" You fix your eyes and blink a few times because you cannot grasp what your eyes are beholding. The picture cannot portray the true image that I saw because it has a blur from the hard plastic windowpane. But seeing that big demon in the sky ready to devour a small animal scared me. My pastor called it "The Sacrificial Lamb."

In Ephesians 6:11-13, God tells us,

Put on the whole armour of God, that ye may be able
to stand against the wiles of the devil. For we wrestle
not against flesh and blood, but against principalities,
against power, against the rulers of the darkness
of this world, against spiritual wickedness in high
places. Wherefore take unto you the whole armour of
God, that ye may be able to withstand in the evil day,
and having done all, to stand.

In the last days, when the apocalypse of the four
horsemen conquers the earth, there also shall the Antichrist,
War, Famine, and Death appear. A few will be able to see what
is in the sky but, if you try to point them out to others, they
will quickly disappear. I have witnessed such occurrences with
my husband, with my pastor, and a few others at church. After
showing my pastor the image from the plane and the other one
with the man, the moon, and the pyramid, I walked outside to
leave. Somehow, I had forgotten to tell her about some family
members with Covid-19 and wanted to ask for her prayers. As
we walked outside, I pointed to the area where I stood gazing
into the sun and where I had seen the angel. Suddenly, the
Holy Spirit said, "Look at the sky!" A big bright angel was
there but, as I turned to tell my pastor, the angel quickly went

away.

She said, "I do not see anything."

And she did not. It disappeared so fast that I looked foolishly standing there. I believe when I see such a phenomenon, it is not for anyone else to see. God will allow them to see only what He wants them to see. But had I taken a picture instead, the angel would have still been there.

This angel, in particular, changed form so swiftly that by the time my pastor started to look, it had dwindled so much that it almost looked like a serpent. The Holy Spirit will allow me to take some pictures, but this one (along with the angel I had seen in the sky over my backyard), I could not. That is because I had invited others to see it and it was meant for me to see alone.

Here is the picture from the airplane. It looks as though a big creature is about to devour a small animal in a mountainous area. The image reminded me of when Jesus was on the mountain top, and Satan tried to tempt Him. I can see why my pastor called it "The Sacrificial Lamb." This animal was sacrificing his life for those around him.

Donna Hodges

CHAPTER 32: SPIRITUAL REST

Come unto me, all ye that labour and are heavy laden, and I will give you rest. Take my yoke upon you, and learn of me; for I am meek and lowly in heart: and ye shall find rest unto your souls. For my yoke is easy and my burden is light.

Matthew 11:28-30

Reflecting on the Word of God, He is trying to tell us that, no matter the circumstances in our lives, nothing is impossible for Him. God wants us to rely on Him and place our burdens in His hands. The Holy Spirit will be the light at the end of the tunnel in times of pain and suffering.

With all the craziness of the coronavirus, the world fears what they cannot see. And this fear encompasses many that profess Christ to stay home and hide, praying that the inevitable will not harm them. God does not want us to be afraid. He said in His Word in Psalm 91:10-11, "There shall no evil befall thee, neither shall any plague come nigh thy dwelling. For He shall give his angels charge over thee, to keep thee in all thy ways." God wants us to take charge and stand strong in times of trouble. God is looking for those who can withstand any problem placed before them so that He can build His army to fight against the wiles of the devil.

As you recall in the book of Revelation, God had to kick Satan out of heaven because he thought he was better than God. Not only that, but He also kicked out those that followed Satan. There are good angels and bad ones as well. Those that follow Satan are angels of destruction. God is building His army of angels so that we can tear down the walls that the devil has built. Of course, this will not be easy. We will have to face many obstacles. But, if we resist the devil, stand boldly, find strength in those that believe and trust in God, plead that the Blood of Jesus Christ stays over us, and continuously pray, we can face anything that comes our way.

An example of this is listening to every broadcast referencing what they perceive to be going on in the world. God said in His Word, "Every one that says, 'Abba Father,' is not of Him." Be attentive to His Word, the true message of

God. God provided us with His Word, which is the Holy Bible so that we can be aware of our surroundings. If you know the Scripture, then you will know that the plagues of Exodus and Revelation are slowly coming to pass. But no man knows when God will allow things to happen. It says so in Matthew 24:36: "But of that day and hour knoweth no man, no, not the angels of heaven, but my Father only." If man knew, they would try and pray before the day of refuge comes.

A prophetess friend of mine told me that her body felt fatigued and worn. As she continued to talk to me, the Holy Spirit said, "Tell her she needs to rest." Then, she told me that she felt the same way.

"I have been listening to one messenger after another on TV, and they are sending mixed messages," she told me.

The Holy Spirit said, "Tell her that she had been listening to so many messengers say different things, she needs a spiritual rest."

She agreed.

Whether we leave this earth in pieces or peacefully, God has us covered by His Blood. God did not say, because we are a child of the king, we would be spared from the trials and tribulations of this world or exempt from pain and suffering.

In God's eyes, we are all His children, and His love for us is equally divided.

In all that we do, God wants us to "rest." Do not try and figure out what the next step will be; God is in control. No man can determine when things will end. Man looks to science to try and figure it out, but even they do not know. Only God can and will decide when enough is enough to spare the ones that are left the snares of this virus. When God feels like we have learned from our mistakes, He and only He will shut down the virus. He wants us to stay vigilant, get our spiritual rest, and focus on His Word. For what is to come is much greater than we can possibly imagine.

CHAPTER 33: WHEN THE LORD SPEAKS

Hear attentively the noise of his voice, and the sound
that goeth out of his mouth. He directeth it under the
whole heaven, and his lightning unto the ends of the
earth. After it a voice roareth: he thundereth with the
voice of his excellency; and he will not stay them
when his voice is heard.

Job 37:2-4

When the Lord speaks, will you be a listener of His
voice? Will you obey what saith the Lord? Sometimes when
God speaks to us, we are too busy doing other things or try to
block what He is trying to tell us. A lot of times, we may not
understand, but we must adhere to the voice of God.

It could be a simple mistake that we are about to make,
or danger may be in our path. We miss our blessings when we
do not open our hearts and minds to hear what God has to say.

On August 7, 2020, I kept trying to check in for my flight but kept getting an error message. After several attempts of trying to call the airlines, I gave up. My flight status kept saying, "Pending." I figured that I would resolve it once I got to the airport the next day.

However, when my husband got off bed around 6:27 a.m. and left the room, an uneasy feeling came to my stomach. After he returned, I tried to close my eyes but, suddenly, the Holy Spirit said, "Get Up! Check your flight!" I told my husband that I had to call the airlines to see what was going on. However, when I looked at my email to try and check in again, a message was there from the airlines at 5:29 p.m. the previous day indicating that my payment had not gone through and to contact the airlines so that my flight would not be interrupted. Look at God!

Clearly, everything made sense. A few days prior, my bank card would not go through at various stores and kept getting declined. I had no idea what was going on until I checked the messages on the bank's page and saw that fraudulent charges were being made. Because God knew in advance what was taking place, He blocked Satan from making my flight fail. Consequently, I was able to make the necessary changes and make the flight to my destination.

Ask yourself, are you listening to what God is trying to tell you? Has God shown you something that is about to happen, but you are still ignoring Him? God is precise, and when He speaks, you may not get a chance to hear Him again. Sometimes, the roar of God's thunder is a warning of a great storm to come. How many storms have you endured in your life? God is sending you so many warning signs, and it is completely up to you to listen. "Fret not for the day of the Lord is coming." Will you answer His call when He speaks?

Donna Hodges

CHAPTER 34: ANOINTED BY THE HOLY SPIRIT

James 5:14: "Is any sick amongst you? Let him call for the elders of the church and let them pray over him, anointing him with oil in the name of the Lord."

The anointing of the Holy Spirit is upon me. When the Holy Spirit spoke to me on August 8, 2020, He spoke in two parts—the first is in the previous chapter, "When the Lord Speaks," and the second was praying for my husband, who had woke up with a severe migraine. Knowing we had to travel, the Holy Spirit alerted me to tell him to pray for his healing while touching his head in the front and the back of his neck. The Holy Spirit said, "Ask God to put it back on the cross."

However, my husband kept pressing and squeezing his head which made the migraine worse. I told him that I could not do this for him, that the Holy Spirit wanted him to ask for healing for himself. I left the room but, when I got into the living room, the Holy Spirit said to me, "Go back and touch his head and pray!" Being obedient and listening to what He had to say, I turned around and went back into our bedroom, where I saw my husband slumped over in a chair, holding his head. I placed his head in my hands and silently prayed for him.

James 5:15: "And the prayer of faith shall save the sick, and the Lord shall raise him up; and if he has committed sins, they shall be forgiven him."

After I finished praying for him, I kissed his head and left the room again. But God was not finished with us. Five minutes later, while reading my Bible, the Holy Spirit said, "Anoint his head with oil and pray again." I did not understand why, but it was not for me to question. So, I stopped reading the Word, went downstairs, and retrieved the holy oil that was given to me by Prophetess Renay Goodman. As I went upstairs and back into the bedroom, he looked at me as I stuck my finger into the oil. I told him the Holy Spirit said I had to anoint his head, and, without any issues, he allowed me to.

However, this time, the Holy Spirit had me pray out loud and anoint his entire body with oil. Afterward, I kissed his forehead again and asked him if he received his healing? He replied, "Yes." By the time we reached the airport, his migraine was completely gone. When we arrived at our destination, he had forgotten that he had a migraine. James 5:16: "Confess your faults one to another and pray one for another, that ye may be healed. The effectual fervent prayer of a righteous man availeth much."

God was not through with me. Before we left, the Holy Spirit had me anoint my head and my house with oil. I was curious but still did not question God. All I knew was when the Holy Spirit speaks, I must be obedient.

The anointing of our heads came for a reason. When we arrived at the airport, all the car rental places were out of cars even though we had made reservations. I called a friend, but she never responded. While calling a taxi, she texted me and said, *I'm here.* The joy of the Lord is my strength. After we got to my house and I hugged her, we sat down. The devil was busy, but God had already prepared the way. After about ten minutes, I mentioned Covid. She said, "I had Covid." Satan thought he had me, but God had already anointed me and my husband with oil and placed His guardian angels around us. James 4:7 says, "Resist the devil and he will flee from you."

Fear did not come upon me because 2 Timothy 1:7 says, "For God hath not given us the spirit of fear but of power and of love and of a sound mind." If I had given into fear, my mind would have been overcome by it. Although my friend should have informed me before I hugged her, I was not afraid or bound by the condition of her previous Covid experience.

CHAPTER 35: WAIT YOUR TURN

Psalm 27:14: "Wait on the Lord; be of good courage, and he shall strengthen thine heart: wait, I say, on the Lord."

God does not use us all for the same things in life. You must wait for your turn to come. Your turn may be at 4:55 a.m., May 21, 2020, on a Wednesday morning when everyone is fast asleep, and the house is peaceful. You may be having a great dream and immediately start to choke. Remember, it is on God's time, not ours, when He wants to use us. God will develop a message for you to deliver, but when it comes, and you are sleeping, you must get up so you can capture that moment.

When I first started to write this book, the Holy Spirit was all over me. He would wake me up every day, all times of the day, with an inspirational message of hope, deliverance, and warning that He wanted me to capture in His book. You'll notice I said, "His book." This is not something that I created on my own. This book is an assignment created by the Holy Spirit back on March 10, 2020. I just want to be clear about that. Though the chapters may not be in the order by dates, the Holy Spirit placed the times and dates where He wanted them to be.

I was so excited about what God was doing in my life that Satan stepped in and tried to block my blessings. However, the more I spoke about this book or testified about the goodness of Christ, Satan found ways to interrupt what God was doing. He began killing off my family and friends during the pandemic. However, I did not let it consume me or defeat what I had to do for the glory of the Lord. We all know that our time on earth is short, but the hereafter will last for eternity.

Satan will try to destroy everything we do in accordance with the will of God. And one day, just like God had given it to me, He took it back. You see, God saw that I was not focused on the assignment He had placed me on. I had a big move coming up. My husband and son were moving back to Georgia in June 2020. I was so consumed with packing and doing everything else but the will of God that the Holy Spirit removed me from the assignment until I could focus on what He wanted me to do. The Holy Spirit was not waking me up and giving me the messages anymore. I could not conceive what was happening.

So, I began to pray, "Father God, in the name of Jesus, I am so sorry, Lord. Please forgive me and give back to me what I have lost—the words of the Holy Spirit. Lord, help me keep your will and help me to stay focused on the assignment you placed me on."

Subsequently, on May 21, 2020, at 4:55 a.m., I was dreaming, and the last thing I heard in the dreams was, "Wait your turn!" Immediately, the Holy Spirit said, "Get up!" But I was tired and sleepy, and I tried to go back to sleep. Again, the Holy Spirit was stern, "Get up! Here is your message."

He was back, and He was fierce. I tried writing in the dark, but He said, "Get up!" And as I headed to the bathroom in the dark and turned on the light, I sat on the bathtub with my feet facing outward. Then, the Holy Spirit started whispering His message to me:

"Read Revelation 1:19, and in it, you will find the words that God told John: 'Write the things which thou have seen, and the things which are, and the things shall be hereafter.'"

What God is saying is that He will show us things that others will not be able to see, and He wants us to document them so that others in the hereafter will be able to see the goodness of Christ and be a witness for generations to come.

The Holy Spirit was reminding me that, on March 25, 2020, He told me to document everything that He had given me so that generations to come will see His love, miracles, and healings in the hereafter.

When God gave this assignment to me, He wanted me to capture what was going on in the world and in the sky. He wanted us to know that when things take place according to His Word, we will see signs and wonders according to the Word of God. Since I started writing this novel, the Middle East has been inundated with locusts in December 2020, the entire world has been devoured by the coronavirus (which actually began in late 2019), African American men have been gunned down by white police officers and held down by the neck with their knees (George Floyd), the first African American woman Kamala Harris was nominated as Vice President, and a major CAT 4 hurricane named Laura came up the gulf from the Dominican Republic, Cuba, and other places on August 26, 2020 destroying Cameron and Lake Charles, Louisiana.

God is saying, "Wake up!" The only thing that was good was having an African American woman, or woman for that matter, as Vice President.

Man has caused so much havoc in God's world and, because of it, God is showing us how He can answer with His wrath. Destruction does not have to be upon us. We cause the direction God is leading. God literally had to shut the entire world down and make everyone *wait their turn* for peace, work, and understanding. The Bible tells us in Psalm 27:14, "Wait on the Lord and be of good courage, and he shall strengthen thine heart: WAIT, I say, on the LORD!"

CHAPTER 36: GLORY DAYS REVISITED

On October 26, 2020, as this novel began to come to a closure, details about the great Word of God and the inspirations of His comings seem to end the way it began—God revealing the sun to me and all that was inside. As I recollect what the Lord wanted me to see, He gave me another opportunity to witness to my best friend and prophetess, Mrs. Pamela Hunter. We could not make up our minds on where we wanted to eat, so I suggested that we return to Glory Days in Elkridge, Maryland.

Knowing God for what He has done today would not be an exception. We ate and talked for over three hours. However, this time we were wise enough not to sit outside again. We thought it to be odd that the sun was not shining again. As we brought our morale-booster from work to an end, we stepped outside and began chatting once again.

Then, with great preservation, as I pointed towards the sky and said, "Wouldn't it be funny if the sun came out like it did before when I turned around and pointed?" And just like before, as I uttered those words and pointed towards the sky, the sun peeped through the clouds and revealed itself to us. We were in complete amazement at God's work. Both of us, being children of the Highest God, were astonished. How was it that every time I uttered those words, the Lord reveals Himself through the sun? The amazing part about it was this time, the sun came out bold, bright, and shiny. It looked more like the moon than the sun. It was a light greyish color. It also had a black circle around the circumference that could not be seen with the naked eye unless you zoomed in.

What a profound revelation the Lord was doing in my life! Totally unreal! My friend covered her eyes. She said she did not want to hurt them, trying to see the blessings God was revealing to me. "These are your revelations, Donna. Not mine," Pamela told me. It was a very cloudy day, just like the first time we visited Glory Days. It ended with a large raven landing on the table adjacent to us.

Pamela expressed that God was doing a mighty thing in my life. Being used as a witness to attest to the things He was doing allows His light to shine brightly through me.

How awesome is our God! As I took these pictures of the sun, we realized that the sun had a beautiful bluish glow that shown through the clouds in front of it. I told my friend Pamela to take some pictures as well because others would not believe what she told them. She said to me, "These are the things that the Holy Spirit revealed to you in my presence. It's not for me to show but for the book that you are writing."

My friend Pamela Hunter is an incredibly wise prophetess of God. Through her, I have been blessed to know what an assignment is. In the summer of 2019, she also prophesied that I would be writing a book/movie when I went back to Georgia. Though I laughed about it, here I am writing such a book that I started in March 2020. I can only finish this novel when the Holy Spirit says it is finished. If it were up to me, I would have finished by now. But, the Lord said, "It's on His time and not mine when it shall be complete."

At approximately 5:00 p.m. on October 26, 2020, the Holy Spirit said to me, "Do not fear man; for man knoweth not what God has ahead of him. Only God knows what He has in store for us. We cannot prepare for those things that we do not know of, but, with a conscious heart, we can be mindful that

God is Almighty and that He will do what He said He will do."

CHAPTER 37: THE REVELATIONS OF JESUS CHRIST

On March 13, 2020, I decided to work late to help my supervisor. When I left at 4:30 p.m., I got in my car and headed out the gate to go home. As I turned the corner, I was startled by a huge vulture sitting on the ground with its wings folded, looking up at me. I almost hit the gate because distracted by him. Then, it flew away.

March 14, 2020: food was scarce at many stores. I went to the store to retrieve some essential items. I also went to the bank to get money so I could get my nails done before everything got shut down. The scare of the virus had everyone running to find essential items in case they ran out. This virus had spread throughout the world. As I returned to my car, a large black bird flew on a lamp pole and started squawking at me. I looked at it and said, "Satan, I bind you in the name of

Jesus. I demand that you flee from me, you worker of iniquity. There will not be any deaths in my family." Black birds tend to follow me when something is wrong or about to go wrong with people I love. I turned from it, and it flew away.

We must know that the Word of God is bigger than any black bird or any other curse the devil is trying to place upon us.

March 15, 2020: I woke up from a dream about my mother, who had been dead since January 12, 2002. She still visits me in my dreams to let me know that someone in our family is about to lose their life. The dream was about us sitting in church and, suddenly, she fell to the floor. My hands went numb as I screamed for help. But when the paramedics went to pick her up, it was not my mother but a small male child. I could not tell who he was, but I was afraid of what was about to happen.

March 18, 2020, 6:35 a.m.: the Lord spoke to me and said, "I have done my part. I have warned those that would listen." As I began to pray and ask the Lord to deliver us from this virus, He said, "It's too late. Satan will do his part to discourage others. Those that are not of the cloth will fall because of him. This is just the beginning, my child." As I spoke to my husband about what the Lord said, my jeans started to cling to my legs. The hairs on my legs were standing up as I spoke, and my pants were being pulled in.

Twice that week, I had been caught off guard by large vultures with their wings folded in, staring at me as I was exiting the gates at work. Black birds had been squawking all around me, flying over my head as I entered work, going to the store, and going home. "Death is upon us!" I heard the Spirit of the Lord speak. I did not know if my time was nearing, but I do know that I am ready and covered by the Blood of Jesus.

I thanked God for my time on earth and the love He gave me. In a vision, as I sat in my chair at home, I saw myself at work surrounded by my boss and coworkers praying. The Holy Spirit fell upon us, and we were saved by the grace of God. When I got to work, I sat at my desk and started with my daily tasks. Around 8:40 a.m., I left to get some coffee and ran into a spiritual friend of mine, Ms. Renay, next to the restroom. She tried to hand me her Bible, but I told her that I would meet her in the cafeteria around 11:00 a.m. and get it at that time.

Around 10:45 a.m., my chief of staff was concerned about her daughter not coming back home to Maryland because she wanted to go on spring break with some friends in

Georgia. But her mother was concerned because the outbreak of the coronavirus unnerved her, and she was in tears. The Holy Spirit embarked upon me to tell her that her daughter would be home and she will be safe. As I started to testify to her, the Holy Spirit reminded me of the vision I had before coming to work. Though I did not pray for my boss, I did witness to her about the love of Jesus and how I asked God to cover her and her family with the Blood of Jesus Christ.

March 26, 2020: the Holy Spirit spoke to me at approximately 9:00 a.m. and said, "The reason you were able to see through the sun and see the glory of God was because it was the day Christ rose from the dead. The brightness of the light that shined so heavily was Jesus Christ ascending into heaven, and the images that you saw on the right side of the sun were the angels around Him at the grave." How amazing is that!

My eyes began to water. I believe no one knows the actual day Jesus rose from the dead. But hearing those words from the Holy Spirit, I was elated. A great calm quieted my spirit. Receiving such a revelation from the Holy Spirit left me in complete awe. I mean, who has been able to take a glimpse into the sun and still live to talk about it? Or better yet, still be able to see?

I had been witnessing to people since that great day in March 2020. God had been faithful and revealed so much more to me. We must acknowledge God when He is trying to show us something. If we do not, we will miss out on so many blessings.

Then the Holy Spirit revealed to me yet another part of this sequence of events. He said, "You are the one that will document the hereafter and tell for many generations about the goodness of the Lord." A great pain came upon my stomach at that time. The Holy Spirit wanted to use me to tell this story to the next generation of gospel lovers, spiritual believers, and vessels of Christ. The Lord delivered me from my transgressions. Now, He was preparing me to be a witness like His twelve disciples. The difference is, I am not ashamed to say I know the Lord, and He is my savior if caught between a rock and a hard place. I will not and have never denied who He is.

It is no mistake that God chose me. God knew, through all my trials and tribulations, that I would be a witness to everything that He had delivered me from. The Lord showed me that it is not good to dwell on the past but to seek God and pray for those that have wronged me.

March 27, 2020, 7:00 a.m.: the Holy Spirit showed me a vision of a highway filled with terror. There were several over paths above the disaster and massive collisions below. I could see fire trucks, ambulances, and police officers, along with the victims below. When my husband got up, I told him what I had seen. I had been telling him my testimony because my husband does not attend church, and I believe that God is using me to reach him and my two sons.

That day, there was a massive scene on a highway in California where someone tried to drive their vehicle into a Navy Medical vessel so that it could not assist the people in California. Emergency vehicles were everywhere, even underneath a highway. God showed me the vision before it happened.

March 28, 2020, 6:40 a.m.: I fell asleep and immediately started to dream about being on TV. I was telling the world why people were dying and about the biblical plagues that were upon us. A prominent commentator asked me why I decided to come and talk about what's going on in the world when he had had pastors on his show, and they have not mentioned this? I told him, "They are afraid to tell the world that God is tired of the sins that we commit."

He asked, "Do you care to elaborate?"

I told him, "God made us in His image. Man has destroyed what God created."

"So, you are saying that God is punishing everyone for being who they want to be and not what God created us to be?" He asked.

"Yes. What I am about to say might infuriate a lot of people, but it must be said. For too long, people tried to hide who they were. They covered up their sexuality. But then, one day, they were told they did not have to hide anymore. Not only that, but men have also murdered, stolen, cheated, and lied. God is angry. He is furious at how the world has become. If God wanted people to change who they were, He would have said so in His Word. But God frowns upon that because He created man and woman so that they could populate the world." Corinthians 6:9 speaks of the sinners that are not acceptable to God and points out that they will not inherit the kingdom of God. These sinners are fornicators, idolaters, adulterers, homosexuals, sodomites, thieves, covetous people, drunkards, revilers, and extortioners.

A long pause, and then he said, "Soooo, you are saying

that people cannot be happy the way they want to be, and the world is being punished for this?"

"Yes, that is exactly what God is saying. It is not just that. We are living in the last thousand years of God's promise. We are living out Exodus chapter 7-11 and Revelation 15-16. The ten plagues have already begun. When God first destroyed the earth in Genesis Chapter 5, He saw that He had made a mistake creating man:

> My spirit shall not always strive with man, for that he also is flesh; yet his days shall be a hundred and twenty years. And God saw that the wickedness of man was great in the earth, and that every imagination of the thoughts of his heart was only evil. And the Lord repented that he had created man and said, 'I will destroy man and every living creature, fowl of the air, and beast on the earth."

I came out of the dream at 7:11 a.m. because I was awakened by a loud noise in my room. I was half asleep. My eyes were closed, and I was visited by the Holy Spirit. First, there was a blur of a cross. Then, the cross got bigger and brighter. Inside the cross was a face, the face of Jesus Christ. I kept my eyes shut as long as I could, trying to see what the Lord had in store for me. Then, just like in the sun, a shiny light appeared of the sword.

I was not sure what all of that meant, but I knew God was trying to send a message to the world.

March 28, 2020: A friend of mine asked me what happened on Sunday? I told him, "You wouldn't believe me if I told you." But I went on to tell him that I had an encounter with not only the Holy Spirit but with God also. I had always said the phrase, "But God." Now I knew what that meant. "But God!" means that nothing is impossible if you have God on your side. For instance, I could never explain what took place on Sunday morning, March 22, 2020, at 10:15 a.m., but God allowed me to tell it in His image.

March 28, 2020: while talking to Ms. Renay, the Holy Spirit said to me, "Time is of essence." I was saying to her that I was asked for more time. It is better to obey than to sacrifice.

After revealing the events of the sun, many were blessed by what I shared, but some who were not of God, laughed, called me names, and mocked me for what I had said, for they were the ones that never had an encounter with God or the Holy Spirit. Acts 2:19-12 says, "And I will show wonders in heaven above, and signs in the earth beneath; blood, and fire, and vapour of smoke. The sun shall be turned into darkness, and the moon into blood, before the great and notable day of the Lord come."

Now that I have seen these revelations from God, it will be hard to go back to work the same as I left. No man can fathom the ability for me to behold and bear witness to God's revelations through the sun and having the gifts from the Holy Spirit placed inside of me. God gave me these visions and gifts so that I could be a witness to the world. He made our way plain and simple; our path should be easy. The Lord says in 2 Chronicles 7:14, "If my people, which are called by my name, shall humble themselves, and pray, and seek my face, and turn from their wicked ways: then will I hear from heaven, and will forgive their sin, and will heal their land."

The Lord is also saying to you and to me as it was in the beginning, so shall it be in the end. Jude 1:24- 25 says,

Now unto him that is able to keep you from falling, and to present you faultless before the presence of his glory with exceeding joy, to the only wise God our Saviour, be glory and majesty, dominion and power, both now and ever. Amen.

CHAPTER 38: BECAUSE HE WAS NOT FINISHED

Psalm 91:10-11: "There shall no evil befall thee, neither shall any plague come nigh thy dwelling. For he shall give his angels charge over thee, to keep thee in all they ways."

Just when I thought God was finished with this assignment, He threw one of the biggest monkey wrenches into this equation.

The Holy Spirit said unto me, "Your testimony will be your faith in knowing that God can do all things if only you believe."

All week I had been feeling a bit sluggish and was wondering if I was coming down with a cold or something. Never once did I allow the devil to plant in my mind that I could have the coronavirus that had killed so many people. Believing that it was just a cold, when my husband, son, and his fiancé gathered for Christmas dinner on December 25, I noticed that my son kept complaining about having the chills. He asked if I and his fiancé could go to the store and get him some Mucinex.

Without changing words, I jumped into mom mode. Although he was twenty-eight years old, he was still my child and needed his mom. We put on our jackets and headed to Walmart. While shopping, the Spirit of the Lord embarked upon me and said, "Get some Sudafed for yourself!" Being of strong faith and adhering to the words of the Holy Spirit, I purchased some for myself.

When we arrived home and gave the Mucinex to him, I broke off two individual pieces of Sudafed and put them in my purse. I knew on Sunday, December 27, 2020, I would be heading to Pensacola, FL, and would need to arm myself. Florida, at that time, was one of the biggest "hot spots" for the coronavirus. Though I was only there for a couple of days, after I returned home, I noticed that my body was fatigued. I continued to go on with my daily activities despite the way my body was feeling.

However, on Saturday, January 2, 2021, I woke up from a dream around 7:34 a.m. that I could not remember but knew had to be important. All day, I tried to recall what the dream was about. It had been raining the entire day, and I decided to go to the Sam's and purchase a rotisserie chicken for my youngest son. When I returned, and after eating a couple of slices of the breast, I felt worse. I climbed in the bed around 7:00 p.m. and told my husband I was going to lay down for a while.

Then, it happened: I saw a vision of me standing at the refrigerator eating, but I could not taste what I was eating. I looked around the room and sniffed the air but could not smell anything. The Holy Spirit told me in my dream that I was not to tell anyone because what He was about to do would be a testimony for me. Not understanding what that meant, and as I laid there starting to remember what my dream was about, the Holy Spirit spoke to me and said, "Smell your arm!"

Though I tried to smell my arm, there was no smell. I jumped up and sat on the side of the bed. *It couldn't be,* I thought. *God would not do this to me.*

Then, the Holy Spirit reminded me that when I ate the chicken, it did not taste right. *Oh my God,* I thought. *No.*

As my husband made his way out of the bathroom, I told him to turn around, and I lifted his shirt. I wanted to smell his body as I always did. I could not smell him. My heart shuttered as to what the Holy Spirit was saying. I did not want the words to come out of my mouth because that would only mean I had accepted the virus. But I reluctantly told my husband, "I believe I have the virus."

He told me, "Spray some perfume on your arm and see if you can smell it." When I sprayed the perfume, there was nothing. I was accepting defeat. Nothing had a scent. My heart dropped. I had already claimed this virus was upon me and started distancing myself from my family. I went into another room and quarantined myself until I knew for sure that I had the virus; however, I continued to praise God despite what Satan had brought upon me.

As I walked towards my office, it occurred to me: maybe God is confining me to this room so that I could finish doing His will—this assignment that was started back on March 10, 2020. God was not finished with me yet. He wanted me to experience the virus since I had to reference it so much in this assignment of His. Satan would not get the glory for this! It reminded me of the song by Bishop Larry Trotter, "It's only a test you're going through. It will all be over real soon. Keep the faith! Don't give up! It's only a test."

As my body took on the virus, the Holy Spirit had me documenting the events that took place on those days:

Day one (Saturday, January 2, 2021): I believed that I had contracted the coronavirus, so I self-quarantined by placing myself in another room. My office had everything I needed to equip me to complete this assignment. And, it had a bed.

Day two (Sunday, January 3, 2021): Continued to praise and worship the Lord, anointing my head and throat with oil and reciting Psalm 23 and Psalm 91. I alerted my sister, a couple of my friends, and my uncle that I had contracted the coronavirus. The Holy Spirit had already told me not to say anything to anyone but, since I had been around a few people in Pensacola, they needed to know.

Day three (Monday, January 4, 2021): Veteran's Administration Emergency Room in Augusta, GA, 1:34 p.m.: I needed confirmation that I did or did not have the coronavirus and waited in an isolation room for the test results. A young lady sat next to me. Before she sat down, I warned her that I was sitting by myself because I may have the virus. She said, "Me too." As we began to talk, I started talking about Christ and the revelations He had shown me. Jaca told me that she believed in Christ but had reservations about Christianity. "I also believe in technology and the formation of the universe," she told me.

At that point, the Holy Spirit took over and witnessed to her the things He has shown me from angels, the big "X" in the sky, saving me after getting locked in a refrigerator as a child, and giving me the gift of seeing into the sun. She was in awe. I showed her pictures of what God allowed me to capture, and she believed.

Jaca said, "You can clearly see the angel in the sky."

I told her, "The Holy Spirit asked me on that day, 'Do you know what a Cherubim is?' Then, He showed me one." She had to see with her own eyes what God had done in my life. She began to tell me how her mother and grandmother would see things and have dreams. They would tell her, but sometimes it was hard for her to believe them until she started having the dreams herself. What I said and showed her started to make sense. She thanked me and told me that if she did not believe before, she definitely believed now.

Because God was not through with me, I was able to help this young lady find Christianity through the revelations of Jesus Christ.

Day four (Tuesday, January 5, 2021): Psalm 63:1 says, "O God, thou art my God; early will I seek thee; my soul thirsteth for thee, my flesh longeth for thee in a dry and thirsty land, where no water is." God gave me this verse this morning. The devil thought he had me, but he was not expecting me to be like Job or "Shouting John!" as the great Shirley Caesar proclaims in her song, "Hold My Mule!" Because God was not finished with me, He allowed me to go through the trials and tribulations of the world to prove to Satan once again, "You can tempt her all you want, but she is a child of God, a woman of great faith, a strong believer in the Holy Spirit, and highly favored by God."

At 3:30 p.m., the Holy Spirit told me to get my oil and anoint myself at the top of my forehead, my nose, and my throat. Again, I was obedient. Because when we are obedient to the Holy Spirit, God will bless us. As I began to anoint myself with oil, the Holy Spirit took control. He said unto me, "Recite Psalm 23 while you are anointing yourself until you are finished." When I began to anoint myself with oil on my head, nose, and throat, the Holy Spirit took over immediately. My index finger went from the top of my head in a straight line to the bottom of my abdomen. Then, He made a line across the soul of my chest from one end to the other as I completed Psalm 23:4-6:

> Yea thou I walk through the valley of the shadow of death, I will Fear no evil. For thou art with me, thy rod and thy staff, they comfort me, thou prepareth a table before me in the presence of mine enemies; thou anointest my head with oil, my cup runneth over. Surely, goodness and mercy shall follow me *all* the days of my life (not some of the days) *but all the days of my life* and I will *dwell* in the *house* of the LORD *forever*!

At the moment I finished the verse at 3:38 p.m., the Holy Spirit told me to sniff my arm, and I could smell my arm. Then, He said, "Sniff your clothes!" And behold, I could smell my clothes again. Then, I began sniffing everything. I sprayed perfume on my arm, and I could smell it. On Saturday, January 2, 2021, I could not smell even my perfume. But today, January 5, 2021, three days later, I was able to smell my perfume and everything else. Almost like Jesus rising from the dead three days later. What a mighty God we serve! God's faithfulness once again had overshadowed what Satan was trying to bring upon me.

Then the Holy Spirit said, "Write these things I say

unto you:"

Things I Did Not Do:

- Stop Eating

- Stop my daily routine

- Stop praying for myself and others, shouting, praising God, anointing my head with oil

- Stop trusting and believing in God

- Stop testifying and witnessing to others

Things I Did:

- Prayed faithfully and read the Word of God

- Ate regularly

- Kept going

- Drank plenty of liquids

- Interceded on behalf of others

- Witnessed to God's people

What Got Me Through It

- My faith in God

- The Trinity of God the Father, Jesus the Son, and the Holy Spirit

- My family and friends

- My praise and worship

- Jesus and coffee on social media

Day Five (Wednesday, January 6, 2021): The Day America Fell:

Two unique things happened on this day. I received a call at 2:20 p.m. from the CDC. Looking at the area code, I almost did not answer the phone because I did not know the number; however, the Holy Spirit told me to answer the phone. The words coming from her mouth were, "Is this Donna Hodges, and I am calling you in reference to a Covid test you had taken?" I indicated that she was talking to me and, yes, I had taken the test. She began to ask how I was feeling and what my symptoms were, then she told me that I had tested positive for the virus. My heart was at ease knowing that it had already been confirmed by the Holy Spirit. But I wondered, *How did I get it and where?*

Though I had received the news about the test, I did not let it consume me. I did not panic, nor did I ask God, "Why me?" If God put you through it, He will bring you through it. God allowed it to happen so that I could testify to the world what I had gone through and how I made it without panicking. Since I had spoken about it so much in this assignment, He placed me on.

Today was also the confirmation of President-Elect

Joe Biden and Kamala Harris. Unbelievably, on the very day I found out that I tested positive for Covid, something happened in the United States that no one thought possible in our lifetime—an insurrection at the capitol led by people that were upset and angered over an election that the previous president had lost. Was this really happening in God's world? The world He created for you and me to live peacefully in? God destroyed the world before because mankind was selfish and greedy. Man's sins are what has angered God again and will eventually tear down the strongholds of Him. Followers of evil and the antichrist led to this insurrection.

People, it's happening again! Wake *up*! If you have not been paying attention to the signs, you better start. The locusts in the Middle East and Africa, the storms in the Midwest and southern states, the fires and earthquakes on the west coast, the volcano eruptions, and the east coast experiencing the insurrection. Sinners are destroying God's land once again, and they will be punished by God. They think they are getting away with it, but God has other plans for them.

Today, what was supposed to be a great day in America regardless of whether you are a Democrat or Republican. It turned out to be a warzone on our ground. It was the day that

Satan and his angels destroyed America, leaving four people dead to include an American Airman who chose the wrong person to follow.

Day Six (Thursday, January 7, 2021): All was well within my soul. The virus has not consumed me, and God had healed my body. Still, I must stay vigilant and strong so that I could pray for others and anoint myself with the anointed oil God provided for me.

Day Seven (Friday, January 8, 2021): From the Inside

I had awakened three times since 2:43 a.m., and the last time I awakened, the Holy Spirit said two things to me: (1) "May you delight, from the inside, from the inside of me" and (2) "Let your light so shine before men, that they may see your good works and glorify your Father which is in heaven" (Matthew 5:16).

The most amazing thing about both of them is I believed the Holy Spirit was telling me that my coronavirus had been healed. Day seven is the perfect day of healing, and He was letting me know that He has finished with my incubation period and I can go back to doing the things that I used to do.

Through it all, I have witnessed to others, stayed calm, went about my own business, prayed for those that had coronavirus, found out where I contracted it from, and took care of my family.

My youngest son called me a "Super Mom." He said that through this whole process, I never sat down. I continued to do the things I needed to do and kept the family happy. Though they were supposed to be cooking for me, from the beginning, I had been cooking for the family. But God! Only God can make things like that happen and still keep the family safe.

When we submit ourselves to the Father and glorify Him, He will give you the desires of your heart. God had already prepared me for this virus. He began by revealing it to me in a dream on Saturday morning, January 2, 2021, and He literally walked me through the entire experience of body aches, loss of taste, loss of smell, headaches, dizziness, and the works. But I never let it consume me. I did not give it one thought until I received the call from CDC on Wednesday afternoon confirming what the Holy Spirit had already told me, "You have Covid-19."

I will not lie. It took me back for a moment because I kept telling people that I was covered by the Blood of Jesus Christ. But the Holy Spirit reminded me that we are all covered by the Blood of Jesus Christ, and none of us are exempt from the trials and tribulations of the world. He also covered me with a cherubim just like He said He would on March 22, 2020. He placed His angels all around me for protection. No matter what Satan tried to throw my way, God blocked it. However, God allowed me to go through this process because I had spoken about it so much in this assignment, and I had to go through it and be a witness to others that if you trust God, He will bring you through anything. Nothing is impossible for God.

CHAPTER 39: TESTED FAITH

To say my faith had been tested is an understatement. I never thought that serving God and having access to the Holy Spirit would end with so much grief, sorrow, and pain. But no matter how hard life gets or how difficult the road may be, my faith in God will never change. I will not allow life to consume me. I will push toward the goals God has for me no matter what the charge. The worst years of my life have been 2002, 2018, and 2021. I actually thought when my mother passed in January 2002, my life would be shattered forever. But God kept me. He knew my sorrows and my pain, but He did not let it shatter my life.

However, during the past few years, I felt like Job. He lost everything, but he kept going. He did not let what Satan threw at him take away his faith in God. In May 2018, I lost my father-in-law. Two months later, God came for my earthly father, leaving me devastated and wanting to give up hope. But I never gave up on God. Satan thought he had me, but God gave me strength, and I am here today because of His grace and mercy.

Over the last few years, I had lost so many relatives and friends that I thought I would not go on. But God! He was not going to let me wallow in my sorrows. One of the hardest losses (besides my parents) that I had to endure was on September 8, 2020: my favorite uncle on my mother's side. Then, God was not through with the hurt I had to endure. On January 15, 2021, I lost my favorite brother-in-law, Jeffery Hodges. I began thinking, *What kind of love would allow you to sustain so much grief and hardship and, yet, you continue to worship and give Him praise?* Agape love. That's what! If you do not have the love of Jesus Christ in your heart, you will never be able to endure the pain I have suffered and be able to praise God the way I do.

CHAPTER 40: MAKING SENSE OF IT ALL

Jeremiah 1:5: "Before I formed thee in the belly I knew you; and before thou camest forth out of the womb I sanctified you, and I ordained thee a prophet unto the nations."

On January 29, 2021, as I sit editing this beautiful novel that the Holy Spirit has given unto me, I told my husband, "It all makes sense." From the beginning, God had been preparing me for what was to come. Still, I never saw it coming. I could not understand why we were sent back to Maryland in January 2016. But, as I put this novel together, it all made sense. Throughout my life, God had been showing me visions, dreams, and revelations. However, I did not know what to do with them. Though my husband fought hard not to come back to Maryland, eventually, I told him, "Let's just go and get it over with."

You see, God had a plan for me in Maryland—an

assignment. It was the only place that all He needed to show me would be revealed. I tried to return to a church where I used to be a member from 1991-2002, but every time I went to the church, it either had its doors closed, or the pastor I wanted to see was not preaching. Driving home, I kept seeing a church that was in the woods from Route 32. I made up my mind one day while returning from work that I would find my way back through the woods and find this church. God was already setting the pace for me.

Even when I first started attending, the church was very familiar. I knew deep inside that I had seen or met these people before. The more I asked, the more I had to know. No one could figure out where we had met. I knew I had never attended the church prior to coming in March 2016, so curiosity got the best of me. Then one day, a visiting pastor came to preach. At the mention of the name Pastor Jackie Gordon, my heart pounded. I knew these people from 1990 because I used to attend a church called Full Gospel Emancipation Church and Pastor Jackie was the shepherd of the church.

I told my husband that though he had been in a terrible car accident while traveling to Maryland, God needed me to remain focused on Him and what He was about to do in my life. Consequently, the key to all of this was getting me to River of Life Worship Center, where the Holy Spirit first revealed Himself to me. It was at this church that many of the testimonies from this novel are revealed. Being able to see through the sun, seeing the X in the sky, seeing angels in the sky, and God showing me the darkness in the sun all came down to Him needing the world to know that He is still in control. Though many have died from the coronavirus, God says, "I am still with you."

This novel started off with me seeing through a bright sun and seeing a big X in the sky. However, on January 21, 2021, while driving down Interstate 240 East in Memphis, TN, around 1:25 p.m., my husband asked me a question. "How much more do you have to write to finish this book?"

I told him, "I believe I am finished because I asked God the same question months ago." I had not gotten an answer until early January 2021 when the Holy Spirit woke me up from a dream and said to me, "Because He was Not Finished."

My husband looked at me and said, "Okay." Then, minutes later, I looked up into the sky and saw a phenomenal view—airplanes making XXXs in the sky. Not only were they making an X, but they made a triangle which I told my husband looked like the pyramid the Holy Spirit showed me in Chapter 28 of this novel. However, the airplane went straight between the middle of the triangle, and when it got to the point at the top, the line did not go close to the top of the triangle. It went over the top. It was an amazing sight to see, and I told my husband that God was showing me that He had completed my assignment for me and was giving me confirmation with the X in the sky.

To this day, I am in complete awe of God and what He can and will do if we are faithful. All along, I thought God was upset or disappointed that I was not staying focused on His novel. But in reality, He was not finished. If I had tried to end what He started, I would have missed the most important aspect of His novel: the beginning started with a sun and an X, and it ended with a bright sun, three XXXs, and a pyramid.

A part of me was disappointed that I was not able to capture the XXXs to the full extent because I was driving. I asked my husband to take the pictures with my phone, but he could not bring them into close view. I believe once again that they were for my viewing, and I was to capture them instead of my husband. God did allow him to take the picture but not the way they were revealed in the sky. By the time I realized what was going on and we had made a stop at his mother's house, the entire group of XXXs and the pyramid had gone away. God gave me my answer about His novel being completed. I only wish I could have captured a clear picture like He had shown me in March 2020.

The other ironic thing about being in Maryland was the people He placed in my life to

guide me. Though my husband and I came to Maryland for a job opportunity with the government, God already knew that I needed more. Towards the end of my husband's tour, I decided to be a part of the government for job security. I was a contractor, and I was doing well. However, after ending my tour in the Navy, I had always wanted to go back into the government but was never given the opportunity. Just by chance, an opportunity presented itself in a rare form, and I found my way in. Sometimes, you have to be careful what you pray for. You just might get it.

Then, God placed a young lady by the name of Prophetess Pamela Hunter in my life. Ironically, we were the same age and shared the same birth month. Though she was to assist me with getting started, after a few weeks, I called her my friend. She was not comfortable at first with me calling her friend, but she later suggested that having me as a friend was one of the best things God has given her. Prophetess Hunter was a godly lady that God needed me to meet. As I think about all that has happened to me while being in Maryland, the Holy Spirit revealed to me on January 29, 2021, that Prophetess Hunter was a key component to my being in Maryland. "You had to meet her," He whispered to me.

She was the one that told me about being a seer. She was the one that asked me about my assignment. She also indicated that she was one of my assignments. She was the first to call me "Prophetess." Though our time together in Maryland was shorter than we expected, we will remain friends for eternity.

Near the end of my journey in Maryland, on November 25, 2020, my pastor at River of Life Worship Center called me into her office. As we engaged in deep conversations about God's prophecies for me, she told me, "Sister Donna. You are a prophetess." I was in complete awe. She told me that God had been using me all these years to see things that others could not so that I could reveal them to others. Then, she told me she loved me and called me her friend. Though I have not accepted me being a prophetess because it was not told to me by the Holy Spirit, I receive what my pastor and friend have told me.

Donna Hodges

CHAPTER 41: DREAMS, VISIONS, AND REVELATIONS

Joel 2:28: "And it shall come to pass afterward, that I will pour out my Spirit on all flesh; your sons and your daughters shall prophesy, your old men shall dream dreams, and your young men shall see visions."

These are revelations that God has shown me

God shows us warnings in ways we may not comprehend. One of them is through dreams, another is through visions, and the greatest is through prophecy. The vision of the angel I saw on Palm Sunday, April 5, 2020, was a blessing and a warning. A blessing for me to see but a warning that God was bringing one of His vessels from our church home to be with Him. When God opened up the windows of heaven and showed this angel to me and all the spirits around it, He was giving me a message that I was unaware of. This angel was my guardian angel and was placed to the right side of our church, River of Life Worship Center in Severn, MD.

The Holy Spirit allowed me to take a picture so it could be evidence to those who would not believe what I had seen in the sky. Though others were outside that day walking on the outside of our church, God only allowed me to see the angel. When I sent the picture to my pastor, Mrs. Barbara Brown, she immediately called me and said, "I see them, sister Donna. I see all of them." At that moment, I knew God was using me in a mighty way, and I was not seeing things in my mind.

Two days later, I realized God had placed the angel by our church to send my pastor a message through me that death was upon her family. That morning her sister passed away along with another deacon's mother. There were eight black birds flying over our church while God allowed me to once again gaze upon His glory. Despite the darkness, I saw inside the sun, and God allowed me to gaze into it.

On Thursday morning, May 21, 2020, at approximately 6:15 p.m., the Holy Spirit sent me to my sliding glass door window. There, I saw a huge angel in the sky and tried to get my cell phone to take a picture. While trying to zoom in, I called out to my husband and, suddenly, a cloud covered the angel so fast that I was not able to capture it. My husband was not allowed to see this angel because it was not for him to see. But it was for my eyes to behold so that I would know that God was still watching over me.

On Tuesday, July 14, 2020, while standing outside talking to my pastor, the Holy Spirit told me to look up at the sky; there, I saw a huge angel. But when I tried to show it to my pastor, it quickly disappeared. I believe that when God shows me these angels, they are for my eyes to behold and not others. Some of them, He will allow me to capture with my camera, but others He was not. These angels were nothing like the angels I had previously seen on Palm Sunday. These angels were spiritual angels that were placed in our lives to guide and protect us in every possible way.

Though many dreams have come and gone since I wrote this chapter, God gave me this next dream as another warning for the world to know that He is still in charge.

Valentine's Day weekend was supposed to be a weekend where lovers, spouses, and friends gather to say, "I love you," have that special dinner, or plan a getaway for exclusion. However, this Valentine's Day weekend, my husband and I kept trying to get a cabin in the Cherokee Mountains and relax. But we could never make our plans because we continuously watched The Weather Channel and saw that it would rain in the mountains. We decided on Friday night, 12 February 2021, we would see what the next day would bring.

But our plans quickly changed as I woke up from a dream on Saturday morning at 8:43 a.m. In the dream, I saw my husband and me on a stalled bus in the middle of a mountainous road. Trees were on both sides of the bus. Someone in distress started coming towards the bus looking for an individual, and I immediately jumped out of the dream opening my eyes. I did not want to see the outcome.

As I closed my eyes again and fell into a deeper sleep, I started to dream about an old workplace from five years ago. Several people were around me, and a message went across the intercom that a big flood was coming our way. We were told to evacuate the building and find a secure place to stay.

As I and others were leaving the third floor, I noticed a lady going down the stairway, so I followed her. It was a shortcut to the outside that I had forgotten about. When we approached the gated area, I planned to get a ride with her but remembered my purse was inside in building. I begged her to wait for me. I ran back inside through the door where I had come. When I reached the third floor, a lady was screaming on the stairwell. She said, "Take me. I cannot make it." Then, she started to fall backward, and I caught her before she hit the floor. I immediately started praying in the Spirit, and she was able to walk.

Just as we got ready to head to my office to get my purse, loud screams from outside poured out. A huge flood had wiped everyone away, but we were up high, and it had not reached us yet. I tried to call my husband to let him know about the flood. He was upstairs at home, but my youngest son was still downstairs playing games on his computer. "The waters are coming," I told him. "Please tell my son to come upstairs." But it was too late. The waters burst through the window where he was sitting. I woke up from the dream.

This dream happened the morning we were supposed to go to the Cherokee Mountains in North Carolina for the weekend. I believe God was sending a warning that a flood was coming and we needed to be safe, and we did not go. Late Monday night, a tornado hit Damascus, Georgia, and Brunswick County, North Carolina. I am not sure how far away that would have been from where we were heading, but I do know one thing, God had sent us a warning because danger was heading our way!

What was supposed to be the sweetest day for lovers turns out to be a disastrous week for millions. Snowstorms and blizzards capsized the entire state of Texas, parts of California, Louisiana, and parts of Memphis, Tennessee. My husband and I were supposed to be heading to Memphis, Tennessee, on February 18, 2021, for my mother-in-law's eighty-eighth birthday but, on January 15, 2021, God called my husband's brother home to be with Him. We contemplated on Friday night, January 15, 2021, whether or not to go and see his brother or wait for his mother's birthday. But God had other plans. He knew what was to come on February 14-20, so He made up our minds for us. God allowed us to see his brother, but not the way we wanted to. While we were in Memphis, I asked the family to have a celebration for my mother-in-law since all her children had gathered there. But we never got around to it. Weeks later, his mother sat in the house on February 19, 2021, stranded inside because of a blizzard that touched down in Memphis. She had no celebration for her birthday—only a blur from the window.

You see, when God tells us something or shows us something in our dreams, He will allow us to remember specific ones for a reason. We must know that God is getting ready to move in a mysterious way. If we are not vigilant, we will be consumed by what is getting ready to happen.

God's message to the world is this: "It is only February 2021, and we have had two big disasters: The Capitol insurrection on January 6 and major weather events engulfing most of the United States. 'If you do not see the signs,' saith the Lord, *'you will never see them!* I send my messenger to warn you.'"

Donna Hodges

CHAPTER 42: IMPORTANT SCRIPTURES TO REMEMBER

1. **Mark 13:32:** "But of that day and that hour knoweth no man, no, not the angels which are in Heaven, neither the Son, but the Father."

2. **Deuteronomy 11:26-28:** Behold, I set before you this day a blessing and a curse; A blessing, if ye obey the commandments of the Lord your God, which I command you this day: And a curse, if ye will not obey the commandments of the Lord your God, but turn aside out of the way which I command you this day, to go after other gods, which ye have not known.

3. **Matthew 10:22 (NLT):** "And all nations will hate you because you are my followers. But everyone who endures to the end will be saved."

4. **John 14:17 (NIV):** "But you know Him, for He lives with you and will be in you."

5. **James 4:7:** "Submit yourselves therefore to God. Resist the devil, and he will flee from you."

6. **Psalm 1:4:** "The ungodly are not so but like chaff which they wind drives away."

7. **Genesis 3:24 (NASB):** "He drove out the man, and at the east of the garden of Eden he placed the Cherubim and a flaming sword that turned every way to guard the way to the tree of life."

8. **Genesis 3:24 (KJV):** "So he drove out the man; and he placed at the east of the garden of Eden Cherubims, and a flaming sword which turned every way, to keep the way to the tree of life."

9. **Genesis 6:5-6:** And God saw that the wickedness of man was great in the earth, and that every imagination of the thoughts of his heat was only evil continually. And it repented the Lord that He had made man on the earth and it grieved Him at His heart.

10. **2 Chronicles 7:14:** "If my people who are called by my name, will humble themselves and pray and seek my face and turn from their wicked ways, then I will

hear from Heaven and I will forgive their sin and will heal their land."

11. **Romans 14:11:** "For it is written As I live, saith the Lord, every knee shall bow to me and every tongue shall confess to God."

12. **John 15:13-15:** Greater love hath no man than this, that a man lay down his life for his friends. Ye are my friends, if ye do whatsoever I command you; henceforth, I call you not servants, for the servant knoweth not what his lord doeth; but I have called you friends.

13. **Psalm 119:105 (NKJV):** "Your word is a lamp to my feet and a light to my path."

14. **Proverbs 13:4 (ESV):** "The soul of the sluggard craves and gets nothing, while the soul of the diligent is richly supplied."

15. **Revelation 22:7:** "Behold, I come quickly; blessed is he that keepeth the sayings of the prophecy of this book."

16. **Revelation 22:18-19:** For I testify unto every man that heareth the words of the prophecy of this book. If any man shall add unto these things, God shall add unto him the plagues that are written in this book. And if any man shall

take away from the words of the book of this prophecy, God shall take away his part out of the book of life, and out of the holy city, and from the things which are written in this book.

17. **Acts 2:19-20 (NKJV):** "And I will show wonders in heaven above, and signs in the earth beneath; blood, and fire, and vapor of smoke: The sun shall be turned into darkness, and the moon into blood, before that great and notable day of the Lord."

18. **Psalm 91:1:** "He that dwelleth in the secret place of the most High shall abide under the shadow of the Almighty."

19. **Acts 2:1:** "And when the day of Pentecost was fully come, they were all with one accord in one place."

20. **Matthew 24:40 & 42:** "Two men were in the field; one will be taken and the other left behind. Watch therefore, for you do not know the hour your Lord is coming."

21. **Deuteronomy 31:6:** "Be strong and of a good courage, fear not, nor be afraid of them: for the Lord thy God, he it is that doth go with thee: he will not fail thee nor forsake thee."

22. **Isaiah 43:19 (NIV):** "See, I am doing a new thing! Now it springs up."

23. **Psalm 40:1-4:** I waited patiently for the Lord; and he inclined unto me, and heard my cry. He brought me up also out of the horrible pit, out of the miry clay, and set my feet upon a rock, and established my goings. And he hath put a new song in my mouth, even praise unto out God: many shall see, ad fear, and shall thrust in the Lord. Blessed is that man that maketh Lord his trust, and respecteth not the proud, not such as turn aside to lies.

24. **Deuteronomy 18:18-19:** I will raise them up a Prophet from among their brethren, like unto thee, and will put my words in his mouth; and he shall speak unto them all that I shall command him. And it shall come to pass, that whosoever will not hearken unto my words which he shall speak in my name, I will require it of him.

25. **Hebrews 4:12:** For the Word of God is quick, and powerful and sharper than a two-edged sword, piercing even to the dividing asunder of soul and spirit, and of the joints and marrow and is a discerner of the thoughts and intents of the heart.

26. **Hebrews 9:3-5:** And after the second veil, the tabernacle which is called the Holiest of all; Which had the golden censer, and the ark of the covenant overlaid roundabout with gold, wherein was the golden pot that had manna, and Aaron's rod that budded, and the tables of the covenant;

And over it the Cherubim of glory shadowing the mercy seat; of which we cannot now speak particularly.

27. **Revelation 11:19:** "And the temple of God was opened in heaven, and there was seen in his temple the ark of his testament: and there was lightnings, and voices, and thundering, and an earthquake, and great hail."

28. **Numbers 17:8:** "And it came to pass, that on the morrow Moses went into the tabernacle of witness; and, behold, the rod of Aaron for the house of Levi was budded, and brought forth buds, and bloomed blossoms, and yielded almonds."

29. **Romans 3:23:** "For all have sinned and come short of the glory of God."

30. **Matthew 25:21:** "Well done, thy good and faithful servant; thou hast been faithful over a few things, I will make thee ruler over many things. Enter thou into the joy of the Lord."

31. **Matthew 2:13 (ESV):** "Rise, take the child and his mother, and flee to Egypt, and remain there until I tell you, for Herod is about to search for the child, to destroy him."

32. **Acts 2:17:** "And in the last days it shall be, God

declares that I will pour out my Sprit on all flesh, and your sons and your daughters shall prophesy, and your young men shall see visions, and your old men shall dream dreams."

33. **Hebrews 12:6-7:** "For whom the Lord loveth he chasteneth, and scourgeth every son whom he receiveth. If ye endure chastening, God dealeth with you as with sons; for what son is he whom the father chasteneth not?"

34. **1 Timothy 5:1-2:** "For God hath not given us the spirit of fear, but of power, and of love, and of a sound mind."

35. **Proverbs 11:2:** "When pride cometh, then cometh shame: but with the lowly is wisdom."

36. **Psalm 91:3:** "Surely, he shall deliver thee from the snare of the fowler and from the noisome pestilence."

37. **Proverbs 30:17:** "The eye that mocketh at his father, and despiseth to bey his mother, the ravens of the valley shall pick it out, and the young eagles shall eat it."

38. **Psalm 91:4-6:** He shall cover you with His feathers and under His wings shall you trust. His truth shall be Your shield and buckler. You shall not be afraid for the terror by night; nor for the arrow that flies by day. Nor for the

pestilence that walks in darkness; nor for the destruction that wasteth at noonday.

39. **Nahum 1:5-6:** The mountains quake at Him, and the hills melt, and the earth is burned at His presence. Yea, the world, and all that dwell therein. Who can stand before His indignation? And who can abide in the fierceness of His anger? His fury is poured out like fire, and the rocks are thrown down by Him. The Lord is good, a strong hold in the day of trouble, and He knoweth them that trust in Him.

40. **Revelations 14:6-7:** Then I saw another angel flying in the midst of heaven, having the everlasting gospel to preach to those who dwell on the earth—to every nation, tribe, tongue, and people—saying with a loud voice, "Fear God and give glory to Him, for the hour of His judgment has come, and worship Him who made heaven and earth, the sea, and springs of water."

41. **Psalm 55:22:** "Cast thy burden upon the Lord and He shall sustain thee: he shall never suffer the righteous to be moved."

42. **Proverbs 27:1:** "Boast not thyself of tomorrow, for thou knowest not what a day may bring forth."

43. **Matthew 6:33:** "But seek ye first the kingdom of God, and his righteousness and all these things shall be

added unto you."

44. **Jeremiah 17:14:** "Heal me, O Lord, and I shall be healed; save me and I shall be saved: for thou art my praise."

45. **Matthew 4:23:** "For it was Jesus who went through Galilee, teaching in their synagogues, preaching the gospel of the kingdom, and healing all manner of sickness and all manner of disease among the people."

46. **Acts 24:15 (ESV):** "Having a hope in God, which these men themselves accept, that there will be a resurrection of both the just and the unjust."

47. **Proverbs 10:28 (ESV):** "The hope of the righteous brings joy, but the expectation of the wicked will perish."

48. **Philippians 4:7 (ESV):** "And the peace of God, which surpasses all understanding, will guard your hearts and your minds in Christ Jesus."

49. **James 1: 2-4 and 8:** My brethren, count it all joy when ye fall into divers' temptations; Knowing this, that the trying of your faith worketh patience. But let patience have her perfect work, that ye may be perfect and entire, wanting nothing. (8) A double minded man is unstable in all his

ways.

50. **Matthew 10:37-38:** "He that loveth father or mother more than me is not worthy of me and he that loveth son or daughter more than me is not worthy of me. And he that taketh not his cross and followeth after me is not worthy of me."

51. **Proverbs 8:35:** "For he who finds me finds life and obtains favor from the Lord."

52. **Psalm 23:1-6:** The Lord is my shepherd, I shall not want; he maketh me lie down in green pastures. He leadeth me beside the still waters; he restoreth my soul. He leadeth me in paths of righteousness for his name's sake. Yea, though I walk through the valley of the shadow of death, I will fear no evil; for thou art with me; thy rod and thy staff, they comfort me. Thou preparest a table before me in the presence of mine enemies; thou anointest my head with oil; my cup runneth over. Surely, goodness and mercy shall follow me all the days of my life and I will dwell in the house of the Lord forever. Amen.

REFERENCES

Winans, B. Lawrence, Bell-Byars, M. "In Harm's Way." Soundful Souls, Black Gospel. 2008 www.youtube.com/watch?v=9a7TUdKgzTo

Raffaele, Paul, "Keepers of the Lost Ark?" Smithsonian Magazine. 2007 December. www.smithsonianmag.com https://www.keepandshare.com/doc/1143976/the-rod-of-aaron-represents-spiritual-authority?

Curtis, Maranda. "Let Praises Rise." The Maranda Experience Volume I. 2017. https://youtube.com/watch?v=S8HFQwsxHBA

Donna Hodges

About the Author

Donna Hodges was born and raised in Pensacola, Florida. As a child, she contiguously gravitated towards arts and writing, particularly in stage productions. After graduating from Escambia High School, she joined the Navy, where her career blossomed in Signals Analysis at Fort Meade, Maryland. Donna is currently pursuing a Business Management degree at Anne Arundel Community College. She began writing in 2001 and is currently the author of six romance novels, two children's books, and one devout novel, *Finding Me Finding You.*

She has published over twenty poems through Poetry.

268

com, in which she received five International Poet of Merit Awards from the International Society of Poets for her poems, "A Gift from God," "Rescue Me," "The Love you Gave Me," "God's Wrath," and "Lost in You."

Donna Hodges has written, produced, and directed four staged plays to include *I'm Sorry Momma* and *Steppin' Out,* which were performed in Augusta, Georgia. Her stage play, *Excuse Me Miss,* though not spiritual, gained notoriety in Augusta, Georgia, and Pensacola, Florida, for exhibiting boundaries of relationship failures and how to rebuild trust in marriages.

After hearing the voice of the Holy Spirit on March 22, 2020, Donna began her latest novel, *The Spirit that Dwells in Me,* during the height of the pandemic. This assignment led by the Holy Spirit allowed her to fulfill the gift God gave her through visions and dreams. She gives all praise, honor, and glory to our heavenly Father for the blessings He has bestowed upon her.

CPSIA information can be obtained
at www.ICGtesting.com
Printed in the USA
JSHW030730220222
23185JS00001B/4

9 781637 696361